Blank page.

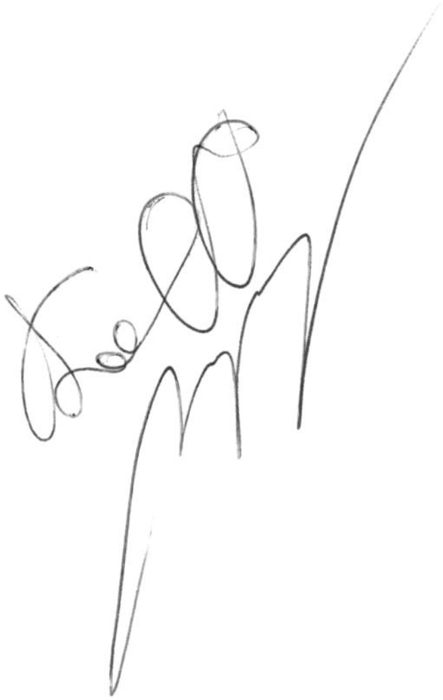

Todd Murphy

Blank page.

Déjà Vu & Other Spiritual Gifts

Enrich Your Spiritual Life with Easy Exercises from Brain Science

Todd Murphy

Laurentian University Neurosciences Program (Associate Researcher)

First CreateSpace Edition. First Kindle Edition.

Cover art: "The Apparition" by Jean Guillaume Martin. Public Domain Image from Wiki commons.

Library of Congress Cataloging-in-Publication Data

Murphy, Todd Raymond

"Déjà vu & Other Spiritual Gifts" / Todd R. Murphy – 1st Print Edition.

Includes Bibliographic references.

1) Neuroscience 2) Mysticism 3) Spirituality

Printed in the United States of America

October, 2017, Rev. 0039

ISBN-10:
0-692-95765-0

ISBN-13:
978-0-692-95765-3

See us online at:

www.spiritualbrain.com

DEDICATION

This book is dedicated to my teachers, past and present. Dr. Michael A. Persinger, Fr. +Nazarin, George Olebar, and Karmu (Edgar Warner), and others not named here. My thanks to them all.

CONTENTS

Todd Murphy

ACKNOWLEDGMENTS

The author would like to acknowledge the contributions of all those who helped in this effort. No book is ever only the work of one person. Some of the exercises and spiritual techniques in this book were tested by thousands of people, over more than a decade. Each one of them made a contribution. I would also like to thank "Sn33zy90", whose transcription efforts were an invaluable help.

Preface

Unless you have it so often that it's uncomfortable, Déjà vu is a gift. It's a strange mixture of the past and the present, and you can use it to *be here now*.

Do you know the feeling that there's someone standing behind you, but when you turn to look, there's no one there? That's a gift, too. This sensation can help you in your prayers and devotions.

Do you know what it's like to feel your body moving when you're keeping still? That's another gift.

Do your hands ever tingle or buzz? Do they ever feel warm or hot? That's also a gift; one that can help you to help others.

Do you sometimes think in pictures instead of words or have images 'flash' into your mind? This gift points the way to intuitions and psychic skills.

Do you find yourself filled with affection when you see a cute baby or even a charming kitten? This precious gift can help you find a new depth of compassion and a capacity for kindness you may not know you had.

Very few people have all these gifts, but most people have at least one of them. In this book, you'll find ways of engaging these sensations that can make your spiritual life richer and more fulfilling.

Most of the methods, techniques and exercises in this book are based on brain science along with some tribal anthropology[a], and some wisdom from a few spiritual teachers.

The brain science we use looks at a few brain parts, and we'll spend some time talking about what they do. We'll take the time to go over some fascinating aspects of the human brain and how it works, but without getting too technical. There are a good number of references at the end and a few footnotes on some pages, to be true to the science.

Déjà vu is only one of the sensations we'll look at, but people who have it usually have other peculiar episodes, so if you bought this book because you have déjà vu, you'll probably find a new understanding of some other experiences you've wondered about. Each of them points to a portal to your spirituality, as well as *your* brain, *your* mind, and your *self*.

This book brings spirituality together with brain science and for those who are interested; it has an afterword at the end that talks about the meeting of science and spirituality.

This book has been proofread several times, but it seems no matter how many people go over it, a few errors always remain. All the proofreaders were so engaged by its material that they forgot to look for typos and errors, and focused on what it had to say instead. If you, gentle reader, notice any mistakes, please let the author know.

---

[a] Usually called *Cultural Anthropology*.

Chapter One.

The Way of Prayer.

Spirit Guides, Deities, Angels, Sensed Presences and Other Beings.

The Amygdala.

Everything that happens in our minds reflects activity in our brains. We feel hungry, thirsty, tired, frightened, happy or sad because our brains tell us about it. All of our feelings, knowledge, and emotions work through our neural hardware. Of course, we experience sensations from our bodies, but they're still routed through the brain. Even if our spirituality comes from outside us, coming from Gods, Spirits, *Prana* (a subtle energy in Hinduism) or the "quintessence" of medieval philosophy, we still experience it through the lens of our neural hardware. *Mental forms follow neural functions.*

Science has found that there are areas in the brain that support spiritual experiences. It's also found that our imagination can have effects on the brain similar to real events. Can we add to our spiritual lives, just by using our imagination? My experience as a brain scientist tells me that the answer is a resounding "yes", but not everyone responds the same way, even when they imagine the same things.

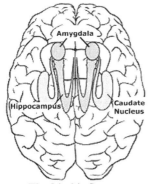

The Limbic System

The brain parts that govern speech can be excited just by imagining talking to someone. Other parts mediate fear, and imagining something frightening will get them working. Daydreams about significant others actually help to build our connections with them as well as building our self-esteem. However, imagining eating a steak will be a very different experience for vegetarians than for people who eat beef. Human imagination can be powerful, but it's not a "one size fits all" skill. Sexual fantasies have one effect for a 17 year old boy who's filled with desire and another for an old celibate priest.

The limbic system has eleven or more parts (it depends on who's doing the counting), but we'll only be looking at three of them: the *Amygdala*, the *Hippocampus*, and the *Caudate Nucleus*. They are the neural foundations for our thoughts and emotions. In my view[a], these are the most important supports for spiritual experiences in the brain.

Most of the primary work on this subject was done by

---

[a] For more information, see "Sacred Pathways: The Brain's Role in Religious and Mystic Experiences", available on Amazon.com

Dr. Michael Persinger, director of Laurentian University Behavioral Neuroscience program. He's published (and I'm not exaggerating in the slightest) over five hundred peer reviewed scientific and medical papers, making him one of the most published scientists in the world. Persinger has also published scores of papers on religion and spirituality, most of which are ignored by his few but vocal critics. He's very dedicated to his work and what we'll be talking about in this book is based on just a small part of it. I'll add that he has been my mentor for about eighteen years. We've even co-published a couple of papers.

Other scientists in the field take different approaches to understanding the brain's contribution to our spirituality. One of them is Dr. Andrew Newberg. His work is based on activity in the surface of the brain, as well as the sympathetic and parasympathetic systems, a control system that acts largely automatically. It regulates important body functions such as the heart rate, digestion, respiratory rate, pupillary response, urination, and sexual arousal. This system contributes to our fight-or-flight, as well as our "feeding and breeding" responses. In this book, we take the view that the limbic system, deep in the brain is the main source of spiritual experiences, but I accept that other systems also play a role.

Everything here is based on "the rule of thumb" that our experiences come from inside our brains; that no spiritual powers or being directs our minds or brains from outside. That may not be true, but the reason we work with it anyway is that neuroscience has already found brain processes that affect us spiritually. It can't find any of the subtle, magical, non-physical entities and forces that might guide us and help us live. We don't have rigorous evidence that they're real. We can't measure them, but that doesn't mean that they don't exist. There is a saying in the sciences that "absence of evidence is not evidence of absence". Nevertheless, if we stay within the bounds of what science knows, we get scientific results. We'll color within the lines drawn by the scientific community, and see the light it can shed on our spiritual lives.

Our approach is focused on brain parts (*neuroanatomy*), not neurochemistry, so I won't be talking about endorphins serotonin reuptake inhibitors or hallucinogenic compounds, like "magic mushrooms" ayahuasca, or LSD. We'll be looking at brain *parts*, not brain *chemicals*.

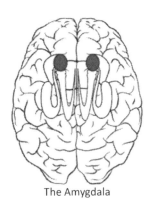

The Amygdala

The first of the parts we want to look at is called the *amygdala*. It got that name because when some early researchers were dissecting a brain, they cut into it from an angle where it resembled an almond. That's what the word *amygdala* means: "almond".

There are two main themes in the amygdala's functions. One of them is *social* and the other is *emotional*. We'll look at the emotional part first. The amygdala on the right is specialized for fear and anxiety. In fact, there are epileptics whose attacks began in the right amygdala and who told their doctors (epileptologists) they had a *sense of impending doom* during their seizures, as if death was just in front of them, ready to strike. The complete fear they experienced wasn't mixed with any other thoughts or emotions, and that made it a searing experience. The amygdala can create some awful moments, but it also supports the joyous ones.

Have you ever had days where you felt so good that everything that happened seemed like a good omen? You lose a dollar and you think "Those who lose will gain." You run into a difficult person and when they go away, no matter how bad they were, you find yourself thinking: "Well, they were my teacher. They showed me that I still need to learn patience. I'm doing great. This is wonderful." You might even look for compassionate explanations for their behavior.

You hear of an earthquake and its death toll. You think: "God is teaching the world a lesson. We can learn from this". The right mood can make bad things seem good. When you're in a state of fear, anything positive can seem threatening. When you're irritable, just about anything can make you feel angry.

The experience of fear, unmixed with any other emotion, is incredibly powerful. It has a sense of meaning to it. You don't feel that the fear is "just there". You feel that there has to be *something* to be afraid of and you'll attach that fear to whatever is going on in your mind, your body or in the space around you, and assume that it's the source.

The amygdala on the left is much nicer. The left is probably (no one knows for sure) eighty percent positive and is responsible for our emotional responses when good things happen. When you receive good news, your left amygdala responds and calls up a positive mood. It can be happiness, bliss, elation, euphoria, or any other good feeling.

Unfortunately, we seem to have a much richer vocabulary for talking about negative emotions than positive ones. All emotions are hard to express in words, but then, no one needs to be healed of their positive feelings. We need to find more things to say when someone is feeling bad. You don't comfort someone who's feeling good. You might say "Great! Congratulations". It doesn't take much more than that. You could add to it with body language, your tone of voice, and the expression on your face, but these things aren't words. When people are feeling bad, they need more than platitudes to help. Usually it takes an actual emotional connection to make words supportive or therapeutic.

The two amygdala support fear and happiness, and they're interconnected through a structure called the *anterior commissure*.

It connects two temporal lobes (above the ears) as well as the two amygdala on both sides of the brain to each other. Most people know that there's a large structure in the middle of the brain called the *corpus callosum* that joins the two sides of the brain, and if you cut it, the person will know how to use something, or they'll know its name, but not both at once. This radical surgery divided the brain in two.

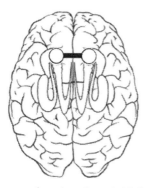

The Anterior Commissure.

These "split-brain" operations were used as a treatment in the 1950s to treat epilepsy that wouldn't respond to any other treatment. The anterior commissure also helps connect the two hemispheres, but mainly as they do their emotional and social jobs.

In other primates, the anterior commissure only connects the two amygdala to each other. In humans, only a small portion of its nerve fibers do this, while the rest of its connections link the two temporal lobes (on the surface of the brain[1]) to each other. When we emerged as a species, it changed radically, to handle the workload from our newly-evolved language centers (on the left side). The anterior commissure does very different jobs in humans than in other species.

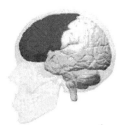

The frontal lobes[2].

The surface of the brain also went through major changes when we became human beings. The frontal lobes (where we have our executive functions) became more complicated, and the temporal lobes got bigger. In order for the anterior commissure to continue do its job, it had to change its end points. Before, it only connected our primal (limbic) emotions to each other (giving each kind some control over the other) by connecting the amygdalas together. For humans, most of its connections are between the temporal lobes on each side, where emotions are processed through the lens of language. The main language centers are on the left, while the corresponding[3] areas on the right contribute *prosody*[a], the "feel" of speech.

It was as though these connections between the two amygdala had to slow down, like going from Broadband to Dial-Up, because serving humans (with our complex cultures and languages) meant they had much more work to do, and now only a small portion of its fibers connect our emotional structures together. The rest of them serve language, memory, and other temporal lobe functions. We also have a set of pathways through the frontal lobes that connect the two amygdala. Information that once went directly from one emotional

---

[a] "Patterns of stress and intonation in a language."

center to another was now routed through areas that control our speech and behavior, keeping them socially acceptable. The frontal lobes help relating to others stay rewarding, by using our social skills and "executive functions". Our emotions are filtered through our thoughts; mostly the kind that can be expressed in words. That way, you can talk about them, and understand what other people are going through, especially when they're feeling bad. Language is our gateway to empathy and understanding others – very important for members of a social species.

We humans can change our emotional responses. You can train yourself to greet unpleasant events as positive forces in your life; as learning opportunities. You can cultivate positive thinking. A gorilla can't do that. If a gorilla steps on a sharp rock, they're going to feel the pain, and be mildly irritated. They can't re-interpret it with positive thoughts. In more technical terms, they don't have the same option to use a positive *cognitive strategy*. They can't choose to think that God is using the stone to help them learn. It just hurts. They might learn something from the experience, but they probably won't go so far as to think that the rock was put there *in order* to teach them something, the way some people think God puts difficulties in front of us to teach us or test our faith, as many Christians believe. They also can't decide that stepping on the rock was helping them "work through their karma".

The amygdala changed at the same time (or *about* the same time) as human culture and societies appeared, and that brings us to the other major theme of the amygdala. It's a social structure. It helps us relate to one another. For example, the amygdala recognizes the feelings behind facial expressions.

Science recognizes six basic emotional states, but there are actually a lot more. They are: 1) Joy 2) Surprise 3) Sadness 4) Anger 5) Disgust and 6) Fear. When we relate to actual people, in real life (instead of an experimental psychology study), then there are a lot more. All the six basic expressions have nuances and moods. "Contempt", for example, is a mixture of anger and disgust. Love isn't one of the six basic feelings, and neither are any of its variations, like infatuation, affection, passion, etc. Science may not recognize all the varieties of human emotion, but the amygdala does. If you know them well, you can see hundreds of nuanced emotions in a person's face. If you've lived with them for a long time, as old married couples do, then you'll see far more than just the six "basic" facial expressions.

We experience our own feelings via the amygdala and we also use it to recognize what *other* people are feeling. In fact, there was a recent case where someone had their amygdala (and hippocampus) on the right removed, leaving the one on the left with more control over their emotions. Their doctors found that they had had become extremely empathetic[4]. The amygdala does more than see what other people are feeling; it helps us create the same feelings in ourselves.

Facial expressions are just one way we see what other people are feeling. Tone of voice is another. There is a big difference between "I love you." and "I *love* you!" and the amygdala is one of the places where we know the difference. It's not just the words. It's a whole ambiance; a mood, or *vibration*.

The amygdala also responds to tones of voice[5] and body language[6]. It sees how people hold themselves; whether they're tense or relaxed. When *you* perceive *someone else's* tension or relaxation, then it's the amygdala at work. Other deep brain areas work when *you* feel them.

Like *any* brain part, most of the connections within the amygdala slow it down ("inhibit it"), and only some of them (about 20%) excite it. Its inhibitory connections "drop out" more easily than the ones that excite it[7]. Psychiatric episodes, epilepsy, the after-effects of traumatic head injuries, *Kundalini awakenings,* and even enlightenment[a] can be caused by a blast (or repeated jolts) of activity through the amygdala. If it's strong enough, it can knock out enough of the tiny connection points between nerve cells (synapses), to leave the amygdala more responsive than before. When this happens, people become more emotionally sensitive, respond to other people's feelings faster, and are more prone to anxiety, elation, and other raw, primal, emotions than before. Even the bliss that comes with enlightenment or visions of God can become more easier to achieve.

The amygdala is the most responsive, excitable and

---

[a] This is discussed at length in *Sacred Pathways: The Brains Role in Religious and Mystic Experiences*, available on Amazon.com

sensitive structure in the brain[a]. A person can become more emotional, introspective, and a lot more empathetic after powerful spiritual events, because the amygdala is dis-inhibited or "sensitized" by losing connections that suppress their emotions and social skills. Some epiphanies have turned people into counselors, pastors, priests and therapists. Others have even turned people into hermits, by making them hyper-sensitive to other people's moods, so they just can't stand to be around anyone who is angry, sad or anxious.

Once, after I had a "temporary enlightenment" experience, I found myself in an elevator outfitted with *Muzak*[b], which is, as one music critic called it, "pallid pap that rots your musical teeth out." It's not music. It has only simple melodies, usually from songs that were popular a decade before the Muzak companies use them, no loud or soft sections, and no strong rhythms. It's designed to *not* get your attention. I found myself in an elevator hearing every note, and wanting to cry with how beautiful it was. This is music that's designed *not* to be perceived that way (or at all) but at that time, anything could evoke a bliss attack for me. Trivial moments of happiness would be amplified, and make me want to cry

---

[a] This is based on blood flow studies, the fact that the amygdala is the most common starting point for seizures, and some of its other features.

[b] Muzak is a deliberately nondescript kind of synthesized music played in some workplaces, elevators, parking garages, and places where silence can be uncomfortable, but real music could be distracting. Musicians often despise Muzak, with good reason. It uses all the musical clichés they most want to avoid.

or jump up and down or laugh, sometimes at inappropriate moments. I was a salesman at the time, and I found myself laughing at the wrong moment once or twice. These bliss attacks weren't too intense to live with, and I could resist them whenever I needed to. Clearly however, my amygdala was less restrained than before.

There are certain spiritual practices that trigger the amygdala's social and emotional functions. The amygdala seems to be the most important part of the brain for spirituality, because it supports the most common way of expressing it for ordinary people; the ones who go to churches and temples. *Prayer* is their most common spiritual practice. It relies on the amygdala's social character, so we can feel like we're relating to the God of our prayers, as though we were connecting with another person.

We know that prayer reduces stress[8], and we know that reducing stress makes changes in the amygdala[9], but we're still waiting for a study that shows the effects of prayer on the amygdala directly. There are many studies that imply it will come one day, but for now, we take it as a hypothesis. There has been very little study of spiritual moods in psychiatry, which led one researcher[10] to write: "Neither Freud nor psychiatric textbooks ever mention emotions like joy and gratitude." The same author also said that "spirituality is not about ideas, sacred texts and theology. Rather, spirituality is more about emotion and social connections that rely on the limbic system more than the cortex. Specific religions, for all their limitations, are often the portal through which positive emotions are brought into conscious attention." So I'm not alone in expecting evidence associating the amygdala with prayer (for example) to appear.

Prayer is the most common spiritual technique in the world. It probably accounts for eighty percent of all spiritual practice. This includes people with disciplined prayers, like saying the rosary or trying to engage in *contemplative prayer*, where you work to shut down your internal dialogue during prayer, to feel God's presence directly; to "commune" with "His" presence. It also includes more casual and less evocative kinds of prayer, like just thinking "good thoughts" or "sincere intentions" towards others or directing your thoughts and wishes to God, as though one were talking to an invisible friend.

The list of spirit beings is very long; God, nature spirits, angels, demons under the bed, the presence of the master, or the spirit of your dear departed friend or relative. In Thailand, some people claim to have been visited by the spirit of one of their most respected kings[a]. The same neural hardware that's involved in relating to other people in our normal moments is also used to engage with spiritual beings when we're in prayer. Here, it makes no difference whether they exist in the world around us or in our consciousness. In either case,

---

[a] King Rama the 5th, also known as *Chulalongkorn*, who abolished slavery.

we sense non-physical beings as though they exist outside ourselves, even if they come from our minds. The mechanisms that support prayer aren't there to show us the truth. Instead, they make it easier for us to learn from our own insights, intuitions, and inner images, and find our truths *there*.

If there is a "God Spot"[a] in the brain (and I don't believe there is) it would be the left amygdala, but only when it's working with other areas of the brain in very specific ways. The experience of God seems to be a *process* that involves *ordinary* brain parts working in unusual ways during special, spiritual moments. If there were a God Spot, it would probably spend more time responding to kittens and babies than reaching out to God.

Usually, we see a big difference between our ordinary moments and our spiritual ones, but the same brain hardware is involved in both. Interestingly, dreaming of doing something and actually doing it use many of the same pathways. We don't have any neural hardware that's *only* for perceiving God. Driving your car at eighty miles an hour may feel powerful, but it uses the same engine when you're driving at half that speed.

Self and *Other*; Self and God.

There is a training program called *enlightenment intensive*, based on the teachings of Ramana Maharshi, a

---

[a] About 20 years ago, several writers speculated that there might be a "God Spot", responsible for connections with God, but this idea has been largely abandoned.

famous Indian Saint. In this practice, the students work with two *Koans*. In Zen Buddhism, a Koan is a nonsensical question that can't be answered rationally. For example, one Koan is "What is the sound of one hand clapping". Another is "does a dog have Buddha nature?" One "Enlightenment Intensive" Koan is "Who am I?" The question can't be answered, because no matter what you find as you look into your *being*, there's always a reason why it isn't *you*. All the answers are wrong.

You aren't your emotions because there are moments when you're completely unemotional. One of them happens when you're dropping off to sleep, when a wave of emotion can actually wake you up. Bobby Fisher, the chess master, said that he could exclude everything from his mind but the game and focus only on his rational and intellectual thinking. Not only did he feel no emotions, but he lost the ability to think in words while he was playing. Emotions can be turned off in some circumstances, so the "self" is not made of them. Our feelings are not our 'true selves'. The self is not our thoughts, because we exist even in moments when they have stopped, like when we're startled. We are not our bodies because our bodies change, while the sense of self goes on uninterrupted. No matter what aspect of ourselves we focus on, it turns out not to be the self.

It's a little like the conundrum faced by extremely attractive people, who want to be loved for themselves, and not just their outward appearance. Ask a beautiful young woman if she wants to be loved for who she *is* or for how she looks, and she will almost invariably answer that she wants to be loved for who she is (or words to that effect). Ask her to tell you what her 'true self' (that she wants to be loved for) is and she'll have a very hard time telling you. Where the self is concerned, we can recognize the counterfeit, but not the real currency.

The other Koan used in this process is "What is the Other", with the "other" meaning *other people*.

The answer, which makes no sense in our ordinary experience, is that the *other* is the *Self.* When we relate to other people, we're actually projecting part of ourselves onto them. We dislike pain, so we assume they don't like it, either. We assume that other people like chocolate because we do. In fact, we have no idea if it really tastes the same to them as it does to us. Usually, these assumptions are (but not always) right. In times of low self-esteem, we assume that others see us as trivial people, because we see ourselves that way. And we're usually wrong[a].

When we fall in love, we project some of our sense of self onto our beloved. Of course, it's an illusion, and it inevitably changes as we learn more about our beloved, and come to understand them as an actual person. In the beginning, we often want to feel them and their presence more than we want to understand them. It makes more sense to loving people because of how we feel when

---

[a] To paraphrase my own book, "Sacred Pathways: The Brain's Role in Religious and Mystic Experiences", self esteem is probably nothing more than how we feel about what we *imagine* others think of us.

we're with them than because of who they *are*. The inner experiences of others are an impenetrable mystery, so we can't love them for who they really are because we don't know who they are (and neither do they), but we know how they make us feel.

If you can absorb yourself in a divine *other*, which can happen through a long and regular prayer, you may eventually become filled with the presence of the deity you worship, even if only for a few brief moments at a time. In Christianity, Islam and in Jewish tradition, there is a strict division of self and God. You can come very close to God but you can't become God. The Hindu teacher who founded the Hare Krishna Movement, Swami Prabhupada, used to quote an old Hindu adage: "You cannot become God. God is already God." It seems to say that by worshiping God, you can come closer and closer to "Him", but never actually reach Him[a]. An inspirational slogan comes to mind: "Reach for the stars and you might touch the clouds[b]." There are traditions that tell us that we *are* god – all of us - but for most, it takes long and arduous efforts to attain the "god realization" we need to truly feel it. I'll say that if *I'm* God, then divinity is very disappointing – so far.

There are exceptions. It happened to *Mansūr-e Hallāj* (10th century, Persia*)*, who is revered to this day as a saint in Sufism. He had an experience in which his

---

[a] Sorry about the sexist pronoun.

[b] It's like the way science approaches objective truth. It comes closer and closer to it but never actually reaches it.

perception of God became unified with his perception of himself. The amygdala supports your own emotions as well as your perceptions of other people, you can imagine how this might happen if these two functions get fully integrated. He decided that he *was* God and went out into the streets and announced it to people saying "*Ana 'l-Ḥaqq! Ana 'l-Ḥaqq!*" I am Truth. 'Al-Haqq' is one of the names of Allah (meaning "the truth" or "the reality"). Instead of being celebrated for his achievement, and revered as a holy man, he was tortured and executed for blasphemy.

I saw my Lord with the eye of the heart.
I asked, 'Who are You?'
He replied, 'You'. – *Mansūr-e Ḥallāj*

Likewise, Jesus said "I and the Father are one". Conservative Jews of his time didn't take the news any better than Mansur-e's neighbors. Rocking the boat can be risky in religion, as Jesus found when he staged a one-man riot in the Temple of Jerusalem.

Caveat: The execution of Jesus

When Jesus drove the money-changers out of the temple, he was disturbing an arrangement that allowed the Romans to use their currency in Judea, but without using Roman coins, with their "graven images" of the emperor, as donations to the Temple of Jerusalem, which would violate Jewish law. He broke up a number of the banks that functioned to exchange the coins, which helped to keep peace in Jerusalem. They were small banks, but they were important for the religion (and politics) of its day. I suspect that anyone who attacked this arrangement would have been seen as undermining Roman authority, and executed. Of course, it would have been convenient for the Jewish authorities to insist it was the Roman's responsibility, and for the Romans to insist that is was a matter for the Jewish government, because Roman law was being used around a Hebrew temple. Jesus could have easily been transferred back and forth between the two (as happened between King Herod and Pontius Pilate) until the jurisdiction was decided, as the gospels record. But let's return to our subject.

Discipleship, with its intimate and compelling *self and other* relationship, can also create strange or just unusual changes in the sense of self. The more you become absorbed in your teacher, (*Tzaddik, Starets, Pir, religious mentor, spiritual director,* or *guru*) the more you'll want be to *be* the kind of person that absorbs their teachings well, or even be like them.

I was once so close to a spiritual teacher that I had a body ("somatic") hallucination where I felt that my face was his face - I instantly knew whose face was superimposed on mine, because he had a prominent nose. It happened several times. There was no mistaking it. I had 'become' him – if only in part. The only other person that happened with was a woman who was also close to him. In both cases, I felt like I was 'becoming' the other person. It was a nice experience, though a little perplexing.

Anything in the brain that works to help us relate to

other people can also be used to relate to God, or any other spiritual being. You don't have one 'love' brain center to love your children, and another to love God. The same brain parts are working to support both.

Recitation, reciting scriptural quotations, poetry or stories, is another practice that appears to activate the amygdala and help people make *self and other* (both spiritual and loving relationships with others) deeper. It wasn't long ago in human history that few people could read or write, and there were far fewer kinds of entertainment. A good speaker, storyteller, or preacher was appreciated much more before our world was filled with newspapers, television, movies, and social media. Perhaps the importance of spoken arts in our early evolutionary history gave us a need to *appreciate* language as well as to use it well. It might explain why so many people want to be actors, in spite of how few jobs there are for them.

When we spend time reciting words that *mean* something to us - out loud - we're using neural hardware that evolved for relating to other people. If we say the words with feeling – using the proper tones of voice – we recruit the amygdala into the process, with its ability to match *meaningfulness*[a] and emotions to words[11]. In fact, it doesn't even need words; it can also respond to emotional grunts[12].

---

[a] *Meaningfulness*, in this case, refers to recognizing whether an event, (including hearing other people's words) 'mean' something good or bad for us; a threat or a benefit.

Some of the world's classical prayers (outside of Hinduism, where brief chants are used as prayers) are fairly lengthy. The Our Father is a long prayer.

> Our Father, who art in Heaven, hallowed be thy name. Thy Kingdom come; thy will be done, on earth, as it is in heaven. Give us this day our daily bread and forgive us our trespasses as we forgive those who trespass against us. And lead us not into temptation, but deliver us from evil, for thine is the kingdom, the power and the glory, world without end. Amen.

So is the Hebrew Shabbat Prayer (here without the notations for sipping the wine, washing your hands, and cutting the bread), which tells of how God rested after the creation.

> Blessed are you, Lord, our God, sovereign of the universe, who has sanctified us with His commandments and commanded us to light the lights of Shabbat. (Amen)
>
> And there was evening and there was morning, a sixth day. The heavens and the earth were finished, the whole host of them. And on the seventh day God completed his work that he had done and he rested on the seventh day from all his work. And God blessed the seventh day, and sanctified it because in it he had rested from all his work that God had created to do. Blessed are you, Lord, our God, sovereign of the universe who creates the fruit of the vine (Amen). Who made all things exist through His word (Amen). Blessed are You, Lord, our God, King of the Universe who sanctifies us with his commandments, and has been pleased with us. You have lovingly and willingly given us Your holy Shabbat as an inheritance, in memory of

creation because it is the first day of our holy assemblies, in memory of the exodus from Egypt because You have chosen us and made us holy from all peoples and have willingly and lovingly given us Your holy Shabbat for an inheritance. Blessed are You, who sanctifies Shabbat (Amen).

Blessed are You, Lord, our God, King of the Universe Who has sanctified us with His commandments and commanded us.

Blessed are You, Lord, our God, King of the Universe.

The Islamic Salat, said five times per day, is even longer[a]:

God is Great! (*Allah Hu Akbar!*)

Oh Allah ! All glory is for You, I praise You, Your name is the Most Blessed, Your Majesty (the power of a ruler) is the highest and no one else is worthy of worship besides You.

I seek Allah's protection from Satan the cursed. In the name of Allah , the most Kind and the most Merciful. Praise is only for Allah , God of the Universe. The most Kind, the most Merciful. The master of the Day of Judgment (Qayamat). We only worship You (Allah) and only see Your (Allah's) help. Show us the straight path, The path of those who You have blessed. Not the path of those who have deserved Your anger, and who have gone down the wrong path. Amen. He is Allah; the only one. Allah helps and doesn't need help. He doesn't have a child, and He wasn't born from anyone. There is

---

[a] Note that this is only one of many translations of the Muslim *Salat*. Here, the translation is formatted to be read only. Actual Salat requires movements and gestures.

no one equal to Him.

Glory to my God the Great.

Allah listens to those who praise Him,
Oh Allah, all praise is to you. Oh Allah, all praise is to You, You are the highest. All compliments, all prayer and worship are for Allah. Peace be upon you, Oh Prophet (Blessings be upon him), and Allah's mercy and blessings. Peace be on us and on all good slaves of Allah. I bear witness that no one is worthy of worship except Allah. And I bear witness that Muhammad (Blessings be upon him) is His slave and Messenger.

Oh Allah, send grace and honor on Muhammad (Blessings be upon him) and on the family and true followers of Muhammad (Blessings be upon him) just as You sent Grace and Honor on Abraham. Blessings be upon him and on the family and true followers of Abraham. Blessings be upon him. Surely, You are praiseworthy, the Great.

Oh Allah, send Your blessing on Muhammad (Blessings be upon him) and the true followers of Muhammad (Blessings be upon him), just as You sent blessings on Ibrahim (Blessings be upon him and his true followers). Surely, You are praiseworthy, the Great.

Oh Allah, make us successful (both) in this world and the other world and save us from the torture of hell.

O Allah, I have greatly wronged myself (I have committed many mistakes) and You alone can forgive sins, so grant me Your forgiveness and have mercy on me. You are the forgiving and Merciful One.

> Oh Allah, we ask You for help and seek Your forgiveness, and we believe in You and have trust in You, and we praise You in the best way and we thank You and we are not ungrateful to You, and we turn away from those who disobey You.

> O Allah, we worship You only and pray to You and prostrate ourselves (bow down) before You, and we run towards You and serve You, and we hope to receive your mercy, and we fear your punishment. Surely, the disbelievers will receive your punishment.

Few Non-Muslims appreciate how much discipline prayer needs in Islam, how much time is given over to it, or how deeply its prayers can affect people. People whose prayers are just short requests ("Lord, won't you buy me a Mercedes Benz?"[a]) won't understand. Prayer is a way of acting out the self-and-other relationship. It works on your mind in one way when you focus on yourself, and another way when you focus on the *other*. All theistic traditions agree; prayer and narcissism don't mix.

I suspect that traditional prayers are so long so that they can be more like real conversations than words exchanged in passing. Over time, it would make a relationship with God become more like a friendship and less like a casual acquaintance. Befriending God means spending time with him, just as it is with other people.

Being in love makes you focus on the other person. The

---

[a] Janis Joplin, a rock singer from the late 1960s.

glow of romance fades a bit when the overwhelming focus on the other person is lost. In the same way, prayer focused on yourself, with requests that your needs and desires be granted, won't draw you in the way prayers focused on God can. This may be why so many of the traditional prayers of Islam, Judaism, and Christianity sing God's praises. It's also why all theistic traditions enjoin their followers to love God; so that their prayers can recruit the attitudes we have when we love someone.

> Great is the LORD, and highly to be praised, And His greatness is unsearchable. (Psalm 145:3)

When we tell God how great he is we focus on H*im* and not ourselves. It doesn't help him, because either he's God, or he doesn't exist, but it does help us, just as being in love ennobles the lover. The chivalric love of the knight for his "lady fair" isn't based on actual romance. The true knight was supposed to happily undergo the pain of unrequited love for his fair lady in order to protect her honor. Of course, that was in mythology, not real medieval royal courts. The myth survives because it reflects a real experience, showing us an ideal we can imitate, but that no one expects us to attain, as we relate to God through prayer.

The intimacy and fulfillment we find from being in love involves something poets and mystics call *forgetting ourselves*. So does the slow and steady "growth in prayer" Christians talk about. Prayer is a self-and-other (*I and Thou*) experience. With time and practice, it makes changes that will always favor either the self or the experience of the other. If we pray for ourselves, we reinforce our self-importance ("ego"), but when we pray about others (including about God as we tell him how great he is), we tend to reinforce positive ways of thinking about them, and refresh our positive emotions about them. In other words, prayer helps us rehearse our compassion, kindness, forgiveness, and the pride we take in seeing others do well. Keeping these attitudes fresh in our minds helps us relate to others in ways that make us and the people around us feel good. Quality prayer keeps us ready for quality relationships with other people. "The family that prays together, stays together."

For ordinary people (not contemplative monks and nuns) the fruits of prayer can appear in how they relate to others, whether God exists or not. Prayer helps us become more personable; get along well with others, and even become an "alpha" person. Our species' natural leadership style, developed in tribal cultures, involves seeing the best in everyone, praising people in front of their community, feeling love and compassion for others, while showing wisdom in what we say to them. Prayer tends to nurture these social qualities, which help us get and keep the respect of others[a]. Meditation is much more introspective and soul-searching, so to speak. Theistic traditions are all sure that we're better off when we pay more attention to the *other* than we do to ourselves. So are teenagers in love. So are the

---

[a] Unless it's your boss in a large corporation, where abusive managers are all too common, but we're talking about leadership, not power.

mothers of newborn infants. "Love thy neighbor as you love thyself."

Suddenly these phrases, focused on the deity instead of the one who says the prayer, make sense, whether God exists or not:

"Allah listens to those who praise Him"
"The Lord is My Shepherd."
"Praise the Lord."
"Hallowed be thy name."
"*Thy* will be done"
"Allah, the Merciful and Compassionate."
"Praise him with great Praise."
"God is great."
"Blessed be the Lord" (Genesis 24: 27)
"Homage to the Buddha, the supremely enlightened one."
"Blessed art thou, and blessed be the fruit of thy womb."

Because language is primarily for relating to other human beings, using it makes prayer feel like someone is listening. We "talk to ourselves" even though we know we're the only one listening, but it seems to have much the same effect as when people actually talk to us. It's been studied with motivational "self-talk", and found to increase performance[13].

Religious recitations are long enough that most people can be pulled into a devotional mood if they say them well, *think* about the words they're saying, and *feel* that God hears them. Of course, a cynical mood can short circuit the mechanism because prayers call for a different mood; *faith*. Here, faith means the *sense* that something is true, not an intellectual conviction. If you don't know the difference, then prayer may not be the best spiritual practice for you. Skeptics who find this confusing might remember falling in love to see a similar uplifting mixture of nonsense and objectivity.

Why are so many common prayers so long? Because they need to be long enough to lead you into a devotional mood. Religious recitations can be uplifting. *Recitations* allow you to express things that you can't put into your own words so easily or beautifully. At one time, they were a common form of home entertainment, and children received applause for reciting the 23rd psalm, the Sermon on the Mount, and other inspirational passages from scripture, as well as poetry and prose from secular sources. Recitations from the Koran are still popular in the Islamic world, as are passages from the Bhagavad Gita among Hindus.

When religion is the main force in a person's life, they may repeat its sacred sayings and proverbs for inspiration, and even decorate their home with them. If you carry an AK-47 and you talk about "liberating the workers, peasants and the oppressed", you'll probably remember other declarations, like *proletarians of the world unite* or *long live the revolution*. Science also has its sayings, like "Physics, beware of metaphysics" and "The opposite of a right statement is a wrong statement. The opposite of a deep truth can be another deep truth. (Niels Bohr)" Inspirational proverbs are found in every religion, and in every school of thought, including science.

I don't know of any religion that *requires* people to put up religious sayings in their homes, but it's one of the most common expressions of faith. People aren't told to do it. They choose to, in every religion, all over the world. Desecrating such a slogan is deemed to be sacrilegious, not always by religious law, but just because believers don't like to see it. They have a sense that their faith is a part of themselves, and that it exists partly *in* those words. The symbols of religion become symbols of the people who believe it. Desecrating a sacred object, a holy place, or words from a scripture insults the faithful. Would you like to see dog shit on a picture of your child or your mother? Probably not, even though you don't believe the picture has any magic power, or that part of her spirit is in it. It just feels wrong.

Inspirational sayings and quotes from holy books rely on the power of words to make us feel that we're relating to others, even though we're not. If use words like "Our Father, Who Art in Heaven" then you feel you're addressing the Creator of the Universe, a power so great that you cannot conceive it, and it creates a mood that won't appear in any other way. It's not a belief. It's a manifestation of faith; the sense that something is true even if there is no reason to believe it.

"Hail Mary, Full of grace. The Lord is with thee." If you say any of these prayers with real feeling, and stay mindful of their meaning, you'll start to find subtle meanings and new ways of interpreting them. The major commentaries[a] on rosary practice say that the deeper your practice, the more meanings you'll find in the words. There isn't a single "*right*" interpretation for them. The meanings that come to you when you're in prayer will almost always offer some worthwhile insight, and they can help guide your thoughts toward a more fulfilling spiritual life. This isn't a catholic book. The same applies to any sacred recitations, no matter what tradition they come from.

Hindu Mantras can be long or short (some so short that they're more like chants than prayers). Here is a longer one; the Mahamantra (or "great") mantra, dedicated to two incarnations of Vishnu, Krishna and Rama.

> "Harë Krishna, Harë Krishna Krishna, Krishna. Harë, Harë. Harë, Rama, Harë Rama. Rama, Rama. Harë, Harë."

It's long compared to other mantras, like *Om Namah Shivaya*. *Krishna*; the supreme personality of God. *Rama*; the incarnation of the preserver of the universe. *Harë* means to invoke or hail them, paying homage to their holy names as you say them.

Chanting is most effective when we get absorbed in it and lose track of the meaning of the words. This lets the devotee focus on the feelings it creates. Usually, they're quite blissful, once their practice has matured. All religious traditions that use chanting (like Japa or Zikr)

---

[a] *The Secret Of The Rosary* by St. Louis De Monfort is one of the most influential.

tell their believers that the state it creates are a gift from God. With time, the person comes to feel that the feeling the chanting invokes is actually "his" (or "her") presence. The formula is simple: Chant. Be happy. Know that this happiness comes from God. Love God, and cleave to him more closely.

One easy way to know if chanting might be a good practice for you is if you find yourself with music running through your head. The more that happens, the better your chances for success with a chanting practice.

Some people believe that the syllables of their mantra have a spiritual power, coming from the sounds themselves as you say the mantra. Many religions believe that the deity is present in their name, which is why Christians, Jews, and Muslims believe that God should only be spoken of with respect. "Thou shalt not take His name in vain", and also why the name of God is a mystery in Judaism, where it's hidden in the letters *JHVH*[a], sometimes mispronounced as *Jehova*. The belief that God is manifest in his name is another reason why "blasphemous" speech bothers people so much.

> In the beginning was the word, and the word was with God, and the word was God. The same was in the beginning with God (John, 1:1).

The Bible even identifies belief in god with belief in his

---

[a] This group of four letters is also sacred, and even has its own name: the *Tetragrammaton*, so that people can refer to it without actually trying to say it.

name:

> But as many as received him, to them gave he power
> to become the sons of God, even to them that believe
> <u>on his name</u> ... (John, 1:12)

This icon[14] of *Jesus Pantocrator* (World Teacher) shows his name as ĪC and *XC*, the first and last letters of Christ's name in Greek. The name is part of this image of God.

Most forms of worship show themes that act out amygdala functions. I saw the same kinds of rituals in Hindu and Buddhist temples when I was in India and Thailand. You approach the altar, perform a ritual bow, offer incense, and perhaps you leave some money. You'd have to use many social skills to do the same thing with a person. If you have fruit, (sometimes I did, and sometimes I didn't), you leave that as well, and then you do a recitation. I only knew the most common one: *Namo Tassa Bhagavato, Arahanto, Samma Sambudassa.* – "I pay homage to the Buddha, the awakened one, the supremely enlightened one."

Catholicism isn't a "better" form of Christianity, but it is the one of the oldest ones, second only to the Orthodox Churches (there are five). All these religions (and plenty of others) have a filter in place that gradually removes practices, forms of devotion, music and prayers that don't evoke a spiritual response.

I believe that there is a kind of semi-Darwinian "cultural selection"[a] that happens as religions evolve over time. Practices that don't work are dropped, or fall out of fashion. Hymns, ceremonial paraphernalia, or anything that doesn't help build a spiritual mood is abandoned, and the really inspirational devotional forms are preserved. The histories of the world's religions are full of reforms and additions. Saints are added to the roster of the "Holy Ones". Ceremonies are changed; "mortal sins" (meaning that if you commit one, just once in your life, you automatically go to hell, forever and ever) are re-classified so that they are not so serious (like gay relationships, premarital sex, and divorce). Yes, there are abuses[b] (and plenty of them), but this isn't a book for exposing them. There are lots of books that do that.

---

[a] New religious forms are often mutations of previous ones, and although they don't appear at random, as genetic mutations do, certainly only the "fittest" (more inspiring) religious forms survive.

[b] Interestingly, the financial abuses seen in the Catholic Church aren't as common in the Orthodox Churches. I suspect this is because the foundation of the Catholic Church is in its priests, while the Orthodox hierarchy is based on its monks, who are not allowed to have any money. Such monks compete among themselves to be the most austere and humble, while priests often go to the opposite extreme[b], displaying wealth "for the glory of God". The Orthodox Church is not immune to abuses and scandals, but when austerity is given more prestige than prosperity, financial abuses are much less common. Prestige, not money, is often the basis of the cleric's "worldly temptations".

Here, we'll learn more by seeing the good side of Christianity (and all other) religions.

I'm an atheist who believes in religion and prayer, but not in God. Once, while giving a talk on this subject, someone came up to me afterwards and said "I'm not Catholic". I replied that neither was I. They were surprised when I thanked them for the compliment. If I can see the value of a religion I don't believe in so well that someone can't tell that it isn't *my* religion, then I must have done a good job representing it.

The Catholic Church has been filtering out of forms of prayer that don't work, the hymns that congregations don't enjoy, and practices that fail to inspire faith, as well as a host of outdated traditions for fifteen hundred years. The Catholic Church once sold *indulgences[a]* and forgave sins in exchange for payment in cash; practices that have been abolished. The Catholic Bible is now available in English, where once owning a Bible in the vernacular could get you burned at the stake. "Flagellation"; beating one's self with a whip, has been abandoned[b], though a few might still practice it on their own. Pope John Paul II did so[15], but in secret.

There is a ritually correct way to enter a Catholic

---

[a] An indulgence is a way to reduce the amount of punishment one has to undergo for the sins they've committed.

[b] 1349 Pope Clement VI condemned flagellation, as did the Council of Constance (1414–18). The practice began as an attempt to atone for the sins that were thought to have precipitated the Black Plague in the 13th century.

Church. First, you go to the font that holds holy water before entering the sanctuary, and anoint yourself with it by making the sign of the Cross. Then you go into the sanctuary and as you walk in front of the altar, you genuflect, going down on one knee, and make the sign of the cross once again. By this time you have performed three ritual actions.

The Orthodox way of making the Sign of the Cross[16], using three fingers.

The ablution with holy water invokes God's blessing. You cross yourself, recalling the crucifixion, and your genuflection shows your humility before God. After you've done this ritual, you come to the altar. You sit in the pew and you assume the ritual posture of kneeling with your hands folded in front of you, and then, *and only then,* you pray. "Hail Mary, full of grace." etc. You perform three or four ritual actions in a row. If you're sincere, these actions help put you in the mood to talk to God, and trick you into dropping the obstacles to your own wisdom, without your ever knowing it.

You need to invoke the right mood. The same words won't have the same impact in other contexts.

If you are praying in a church, and someone says "your car just got a dent in the fender", you'll be much less likely to get upset about it. If you're absorbed in your prayers, you might even let it pass. The same applies to

Temples, Synagogues, Mosques, Sweat Lodges, and Sacred Circles. You're supposed to forget the outside world when you enter them.

It's a sacred moment in a sanctified space, and without it being an explicit rule of any religion I know of, you try not to allow profane thoughts when you are in a sacred mood. As a child, I was told "don't think about girls when you're praying", but I was too young to understand what it really meant. Eventually, I realized that it can be a significant distraction, but by then I was no longer "in the church". My point here is that the traditional rites, rituals, symbols and scriptures do their job. When they are used with sincerity (or with faith, an ineffable prerequisite), they invoke a spiritual mood.

Hearing inner voices is another phenomenon that involves the amygdala[17], though most of its neural support is in other areas. Here, we're touching the line between the sacred and the psychiatric. The Catholic church has had fifteen hundred years to learn which issues were common enough that priests would eventually encounter them, and its been giving pastoral counseling for people who "hear voices" for a very long time. When a religious phenomenon happened often enough, priests were given some education about how to respond when people said they had it. The Carmelite, Saint John of the Cross, advised that inner voices usually shouldn't be trusted, but that such "locutions" are more valuable when they appear during prayer. In the end, he advised that those that have them should return to their own sense of morality and ethics. Common sense, he said, should decide whether they were sinful or virtuous. The voices themselves are *never* the authority for deciding whether they should be believed. Saint Paul of Tarsus said about the same thing.

Today, the church advises that the person should seek out psychiatric counseling. Of course this could have to do with the fact that the Catholic Church just doesn't want to put its priests at risk for being accused of practicing medicine without a license, now that hearing voices is a medical symptom, and not a sign of *grace* or demonic assaults. In any case, divine locutions, the *voice of the devil*, and schizophrenic vocal hallucinations all have the same neural bases. They're supported by many of the same pathways in the brain. Today, it's often called "channeling", and it's regaining its sacred character for a lot of people, though there are still plenty who'll call it a "tool of the devil".

There are many kinds of "invisible beings". Monsters in the closet, the spirit of your dead relatives, God himself, the Lord and Master of the universe, the blessed holy virgin Mary, Shiva, or Ganesh. There are many traditions and teachers, Osho for one, who say that spirituality is divided into two basic parts: the way of prayer, and the way of meditation. Broadly speaking, the amygdala "drives" the way of prayer, but never by itself. There are many other brain areas involved, and the connections are different for different people, which is why these apparitions are usually different for everyone.

An episode of a non-physical being is usually a powerful one. Now we'll look at a much more subtle version of the same experience. It's milder, but much more common.

The Sensed Presence Exercise

The mildest and most common sign of an aptitude for the "way of prayer" is a neurological (and often spiritual) event called *the sensed presence* (sometimes it's called a "feeling of presence"). Have you ever had the feeling that there was someone or a living being behind you, but when you turned to look, no one was there? Most people have had this happen at least a few times. Some never have it at all. A few have it almost constantly.

This sensation is the basis of our first exercise.

To do this exercise:

1) Close your eyes and sit up straight

2) Relax.

3) Close your eyes and take a few deep, quiet, prolonged breaths. Take just one step into meditation, or put yourself in a mild trance.

4) Imagine that there is a presence behind you and to your *right*. Imagine it behind you, where you wouldn't

be able to see it, so you can only feel its presence[a].   Try not to label it. *Don't* decide that you know who it is. It could be a spirit, a God, a guru, someone you loved who no longer lives on this earth, but leave that label blank. See who it is each time you do the exercise. Don't go into it expecting any specific presence.

5) Next, imagine a presence behind you on your *left*.

If you're like most people who've tried this exercise, you'll notice a difference in how it feels on each side.

This "guided imagination" works best after the sun has gone down, when melatonin levels in the brain are rising. Melatonin facilitates sleep and dreams. No one has looked into this that I'm aware of, but melatonin seems to contribute to altered states in general. It doesn't create them by itself, but it can give them momentum and force. Some people prefer meditation at night. Others find their creativity is higher then. You may not be giving this exercise a chance to work if you do it during the day.

Once you've developed a knack for it, the sensed presence exercise can be used at any time. This isn't a meditation where you sit in a certain posture, with your mind focused for twenty minutes, doing it once in the morning and once at night. This isn't meditation *per se*.

---

[a] Imagining it behind you means that you wouldn't see it if it were an actual person, so you can leave your vision (and the brain's many visual centers) out of the exercise, so you're trying to influence much less of your brain , making the neurological "task" simpler and easier.

To work with this exercise, simply do it whenever it occurs to you. It can be very helpful in "priming" yourself for other spiritual practices, whether they're meditative or prayerful. For most people, one side is more pleasant than the other. Imagining the presence on the right side is usually unpleasant and doing it on the left side usually feels good, nice, inviting, or warm. I've seen people jump in surprise at how unpleasant imagining a presence on the right was for them, and shocked at how good the one on the left felt.

I once taught this exercise to someone from India who called himself a "born again Hindu". It gave him a brief vision of the god, Hanuman. This range of experience includes any kind of non-physical beings, and if you decide you know what being you're imagining, you'll cut out all the other possibilities. Instead, think of it as a place where you can *look* for any kind of subtle being, spirit, angel, deity, or saint. You can imagine *any* being you want.

Do it briefly, and then stop. Its effects seem to build up according to how *often* you do it, not how long. There's no reason to spend more than about three minutes with it, though you can continue for as long as you want. If you're going to pray, feel the *presence* for a minute or so, on the side that feels best for you (usually, but not always, the left) and *then* begin your prayers. Imagine it for a minute or two just before you begin meditation. If your meditation is shaky, it can make it a little stronger and if your practice is strong it can make it run deeper. I've heard of all of these things happening. Everyone is different, so see what it can do for *you*.

You don't have to limit your imagination to non-physical beings. You can also imagine *living* people in this way. One can imagine a Guru, a spiritual teacher, a lover, or someone you know and respect.

Suppose you are a new mother, and your baby is just a few days old; you can imagine that your baby is in a crib just behind you and to the left. Putting yourself in the right spot won't be the same. You need to engage your *imagination*. New-born babies have a very powerful presence. They can take weeks to lose their seemingly divine character. For many mothers, childbirth and what follows it is a mystic experience. The whole world changes and everything is *about* babies, birth, and with that, the cycle of generations. Babies have no choice but to be sacred. They just can't help it.

When my daughter was born, I suddenly started seeing every piece of art that had a person holding an infant in it, and I found myself thinking *Yeah! Yes that's it. That's what life is really about*. When I was fifteen and fell in love with a girl for the first time, life was absolutely, unquestionably, about something else. Love and sexual desire. It was self-evident. When you're doing a daily yoga practice successfully, then life seems to be about spiritual growth. One day a doctor might come to you and say "I'm sorry, but you got non-specific something-itis, and you're going to die." Then life will be about your health, but when a child is born, life is about children and babies, and the next generation fills your mind.

The sensed presence imagination offers a way to 'fill in the blank' with any sacred presence.

There are no right or wrong presences to evoke in this way. You can use the one that's most pleasant and evocative for you. Just don't work with any that you're afraid of. If it's a living being, great. If it's a non-physical being, wonderful. If it's a dead person, excellent! The only rule is to pursue presences that feel good.

Another Sensed Presence Exercise

In this variation, you imagine a presence on the side that feels best, but this time, you imagine it behind and *above* you, off to the side, as before.

Most people who respond to the sensed presence imagination find that imagining it *above* them has a different and better feel to it. There isn't much scientific evidence to explain this, but it will come with time.

I've added a good deal of background information to most of these exercises, but this one doesn't really need any. Just try it.

The *sensed presence* happens spontaneously for a lot of people. In fact, it's a marker (but not a decisive one) for diagnosing temporal lobe epilepsy, a disorder I had when I was a kid. The sensed presence happens when communication between the temporal lobes (especially the left and right amygdala) breaks down or becomes excessive. Only a small part of the *anterior commissure,* the structure that directly connects the two amygdala, is dedicated to communication between them. It's actually quite easy for to disturb it – because compared to other primates, there aren't as many pathways involved.

When we love others, we project a part of our sense of self onto them, instead of just projecting it outside of ourselves, as happens with the *sensed presence*. This is one of the reasons why there is so much art and written literature about the experience of being in love, like poetry, songs, and entire dramas, all about the intensity of romantic love. The experience of profound love for God is expressed endlessly in mystic poetry, psalms, canticles, scriptures, liturgies and chants. The presence we feel in such moments is our own right-hemispheric sense of self, appearing outside our body's space. The experience "goes beyond words". It's *ineffable* (impossible to express verbally) because there are no primary speech centers on the right side, and because the sense of our beloved's presence and the sense of self share many of the same pathways in the brain.

It's a bit surprising that there is so little poetry about giving birth. If we push ourselves, we can all remember the names of half a dozen love poems or songs, and most of us have encountered a few pieces of mystic poetry, but one of the most intense *self and other* experiences happens when a newborn child enters our lives, and there is very little poetry about it, and almost no songs. We have a song for birthdays. We have songs for Christmas and Hanukah, a new year's song, several Easter Songs and a few others. It's strange that there is no childbirth song. Perhaps it's that new mothers don't feel it's important to find words for the experience. It can be one of the most intense kinds of love, and it's completely fulfilling. It's an infant, so its love comes without any complications. Unlike the kinds of love we find elsewhere in life, the experience is usually not at all frustrating.

Even when it's requited and fulfilled, love is always frustrating. Its not always *deeply* so, but it's never perfect. Falling in love means projecting a part of ourselves (the right-hemispheric "self") onto the one we love, and hiding it behind the screen of *their* presence. It can seem that no matter how much time you're with them, you still feel that you don't *really* know them. They remain a mystery. Enduring love belongs to those who are wise enough to see the *other* as they see themselves, and can forget about how they differ from the person they'd most like them to be. Once you do that, you can keep the relationship alive, but you'll have to accept their bad habits, and tolerate your own occasional irritation at them. We find fulfillment in love when we accept the other person as they are; including their annoying little habits. When the first bloom of romantic love is over, our lovers become who they are, and not who we think they should be.

Earlier, we talked about a practice called *enlightenment intensive*, derived from Ramana Maharshi's spiritual teachings. It asks people to engage the question "Who am I?" for days at a time. However, that's only the first question. The second question is "What is the other?"

and in that tradition, the answer is "The other is myself." This includes *all* self-and-other relationships, and your relationship with God is no exception.

"Who am I? I don't exist." "What is the other? The other is me."

If those two statements don't confuse you and your basic assumptions about life, as well as the habits in your thoughts, then you should avoid the "who am I" challenge and focus on prayer or meditation because it probably won't be the practice for you. "Who am I?" is not a common practice. We look at it here because thinking about it helps show the puzzling nature of the self and our experiences of other people.

There is a Hindu saying "Tat Tvam Asi", meaning *thou art that*[18]. In its simplest meaning, it says that God (the "ultimate") is actually *you*. It implies that the search for God and the search for the "true" or "higher" self are one and the same. It says that "God realization *is* self-realization."

To further confuse things, I believe that the self is a hallucination. It doesn't actually have any existence of its own[a].

The temporal lobes of the brain are involved in creating and maintaining hallucinations.

---

[a] See "Sacred Pathways": The Brain's Role in Religious and Mystic Experiences" by Todd Murphy (On Amazon.com)

One of the most famous experiments demonstrating this was done shortly after the development of LSD. It consisted of giving LSD to monkeys after removing different parts of their brain. Their behavior showed when the monkeys were tripping and when they weren't. I don't know how they acted. For all I know they were in a hallucinated simian field, watching the simian clouds, "groking" the monkey wowness, and the everythingness of monkeyhood. Various parts of the brain were removed before the monkeys were given LSD. They took out the frontal lobes and the monkeys still showed the drug's effects. Monkeys that had their occipital lobes removed still "tripped". Monkeys that had their temporal-parietal-occipital region (where your antlers would be rooted if you were a stag deer), taken out continued to respond to the LSD. When they removed the temporal lobes, the LSD had no effect. It was a very instructive, but still brutal, experiment.

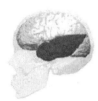

The Temporal Lobes.

I know someone who was involved in some of the first LSD experiments, who said: "we used the methods we had at the time." Eventually, he took it himself and that persuaded him that the methods were absolutely wrong. He said "We had them strapped onto gurneys." The subjects were "tripping"; they wanted to be out in a field, picking flowers, singing songs to the clouds, being amazed at the *wow-ness* of the *all-ness*. Instead, they were strapped to rolling hospital beds, where doctors shined flashlights into their eyes to see the pupillary response, and poked them with things to test their reflexes. It created a disproportionate number of "bad trips".

Now we understand that there are better ways to do this kind of research.

Today, it's more likely that the subjects would be outfitted with a portable EEG, (an electroencephalographic headset), they would be allowed to go out in the meadows, see the flowers and encouraged to look at the "wow-ness" of the "everything-ness", without being disturbed, but the researchers didn't know that at that time.

The *sensed presence* illusion has been artificially induced in several laboratory experiments that used a kind of magnetic stimulation[19]. Interestingly, the *presence* moved when the subjects tried to focus on its location. The *presence* wouldn't put itself at the center of their attention; it would usually remain on the periphery. This happens with many kinds of hallucinations. They often change or dissolve if you focus your attention on them. Drug-induced visions are a lot less fleeting, but almost every other kind can be altered just by staring directly at them. Hypnogogic hallucinations, fleeting visions that appear when you're falling asleep, are especially prone to break up or change when we try to focus on them or one of their details. According to Carlos Casteneda's spiritual teacher, Don Juan Matus, the way to look at them is to "gaze without staring".

Just as it's usually impossible to focus on the *sensed*

presence or a hallucination, you also can't focus on your *self*. You can go inside and look for your *self* pursuing the "Who am I?" question, but every time you find something you think is *you*, you'll be wrong. You aren't your emotions because there are moments when you aren't emotional. You aren't your thoughts because there are times when you aren't thinking. You aren't your personal history because your personal history will change as more is added to it tomorrow, but you'll still be there. You are not your tastes. A lot of people identify themselves by the things they like or don't like, but when you zoom in on these things, you find that none of them are you. These are descriptions of pieces of ourselves, but they don't define your "self".

We can't find ourselves. It's a wild goose chase. Nevertheless, according to some spiritual teachings, you can become enlightened, even if only temporarily, by chasing after it anyway, even though chasing after it tends to chase it away. As you do so, you accept no substitutes for that goose, which doesn't really exist. It sounds more paradoxical than it really is, and few things offer a more engaging puzzle than the nature of the self. Examining the self doesn't make sense unless you're actually doing it.

That's why I think that the self is a hallucination. You can't look at it the same way as ordinary perceptions. The self is supported by the same brain areas that underpin hallucinations – the temporal lobes, amygdala, and hippocampus on both sides of the brain. All of them are involved with the sense of self and all of them produce hallucinations when they are stimulated properly.

There are two senses of self, based in each side of the brain. The one on the right is the one we project onto *others* (whether they're real or not). It happens, without our knowing it, when we worship God, when we fall in love, when we see a ghost or an angel, and when we relate to other people in any meaningful way. It may not happen when we relate to people we're indifferent about.

In all these moments, we go on being the dominant "self"; the one that talks; the one on the left side, where the language centers are located, and where our speech and internal dialog happens. Our sense of the "other" is largely produced from the right side, but of course, each self draws heavily from the other side of the brain[a]. One way we can see how we "are" the linguistic sense of self is by looking at the impact that words can have on us.

They say "sticks and stones can break your bones, but words can never hurt you." It's not true. A simple chain of words can have a huge impact on you and your self-esteem. 'You're fired.' 'I want to start seeing other people.' 'You're overdrawn.' 'I'm sorry, but you're going to have to replace the transmission.'

Simple strings of words can change the way we feel and make big changes in our lives for a long time to come. A simple sentence can be the harbinger of an inescapable

---

[a] There are no left and right brain faculties. Instead, all processes use the whole brain, but 'weighted' towards one side or the other.

calamity. The dentist says: "you just have to go through this. Sorry. There really isn't any choice." These words are the prelude to pain, expense, and a touch of humiliation. "Your cat was hit by a car". 'Sticks and stones can break your bones, but words can *really* hurt you.'

If a child ever comes to you saying that another kid is teasing them, don't tell them that "words can't really hurt you". The world is becoming aware that words really *can* hurt. We're learning, very slowly, that it *does* matter what we say to people. It matters whether speech is insulting, self-centered, ignorant or cruel. In our ordinary states of mind, the self is largely written in words. We know ourselves largely through the words that run through our minds[a], but our understanding of others comes from our *sense* of who they are. We know others through our sense of their presence, and how we feel when we're with them, but very often, we know ourselves through the words we hear in our own minds.

A lot of the things we say to ourselves in our own internal dialogue are based on our *sense* of things, not on the literal meaning of our inner words, and those who understand that we know other people this way can do well with devotional spiritual practices, by building a sense of the deity's presence. Our prayers are uplifting because of the moods they both demand and nurture, but it's an art; a skill. It needs time and effort, and a touch

---

[a] This refers to the ordinary ways of knowing the self, not the kind of knowledge that comes from meditation, therapy, or mental training.

of artistry. You have to get into its groove, and no priest or psychologist can tell you how to do that.

Chapter Two
Space, time, thought, and meditation.

The hippocampus and the things we find in darkness.

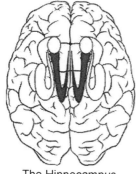

The Hippocampus.

The next brain part we're going to look at is called the *hippocampus*, the Greek word for seahorse. It got its name when some early brain researchers cut into it and found that and it looked like a seahorse on one side. They had to name it after its shape because they had no idea what it did.

The hippocampus is a cognitive or "*thinking*" structure. It thinks, both with words and in silence. Just like the amygdala we looked at in the last chapter, the left and right hippocampus do very different jobs. On the left side of the brain, where the language centers are, it processes verbal information and thinks with words, but it's not the only brain part that does that. In fact, the frontal lobes do more thinking that *we're aware of* than any other area of the brain, and it's supported by (and vastly connected to) the hippocampus.

Most of our social skills are based in the frontal lobes. It's also at the core of our ability to extrapolate into the future; to expect, predict and anticipate things. It's also the main force behind our intelligence.

You may remember being taught about human evolution in school and being shown collections of stone tools. We were told that some of these tools came from a certain culture and we were asked to see how primitive they are. Then we saw more refined stone tools coming from a later culture and we could see how they became more sophisticated. The tools improved in each epoch. The point was to see the development of human intelligence in these stones, but now the view has changed. Most evolutionary biologists now believe that we get a better view of human intelligence listening to stories and songs or seeing the way people argue.

Our main use of our intelligence is in relating to other people. It takes intelligence to make a stone tool. You have to knap the stone and break it into the right shape. Then you need a wooden stick with a socket cut to fit it. You put the stone point in the socket, and glue it in with melted tree sap. Next, you tie it in place using wet rawhide, as tightly as you can, and then you let it dry. After that, you have a solid, strong spear. Making it takes a good amount of intelligence, planning and forethought.

If you want to see *real* human intelligence at work, look at the delivery worker who calls his boss and says he's on the job while he's actually in a bar, drinking beer. He comes back to work after a couple of hours, and explains that he witnessed an accident while making his deliveries, while his cell phone was accidentally set to a silent ring. The boss believes his lies, the episode ends, and he keeps his job. You have to be smart to pull that off.

Relating to other people takes more intelligence than calculus or rocket science. If someone says that your life isn't rocket science, you can tell them "Yes, it's much *more* complicated." We begin to relate to others when we're very young, so we don't remember learning how to do it, and we forget most of our mistakes.

The hippocampus works by putting things in context, like the way one memory can remind you of another ("by association"), or how something in the present forces you to remember something relevant from the past. The hippocampus is smart, and on the left side it knows how to recall words and use them to relate to others. It can also be forced to work in strictly rigorous ways, like in math or logic. The hippocampus contributes to both the most emotional and the most sterile things we say. Talking to people can be emotional at times, whether you love them or hate them. Language is very different when you're writing for a medical journal, where the rules demand that you avoid words with an emotional impact.

It's a challenge. I've written one book that has lots of

emotional moments, I have some scientific journal publications and I'm in very different moods when I'm doing these two kinds of writing. The strictly logical and linear mind-set feels very different from my more relaxed kind of writing. The first is much more work, and mistakes aren't allowed. The first is 'heady' and the second is more 'heart centered', but both are 'hippocampal'.

On the right side of the brain, the hippocampus works with non-verbal thinking. It thinks without words. So if you're a cook, it thinks in terms of smells, fragrances, textures, and flavors as you mix spices. If you're a musician, it thinks in terms of timbre and pitch, rhythm, and melody. All of these reflect kinds of intelligence and thought processes that can't be expressed in words. If you add put lyrics to your music, then you get *some* linguistic involvement, but melody, pitch and rhythm are rewarding, even without words.

The difference between the good spiritual music and songs, and the second rate ones, is obvious to anyone who has heard both, but no one can tell you exactly what the difference is. Why is Schubert's *Ave Maria* capable of moving so many people to tears when they listen to it with real focus?

If you know it, compare it to the music for "happy birthday".

I'm sure very few people ever choose to listen to "Happy Birthday" for entertainment the way they might listen to Elvis Presley or the Shubert Ave Maria. The tremendously evocative spiritual music that can tear-your-heart-out and make you gasp is a different thing altogether. In the Russian Orthodox Church, with its magnificent choirs, the entire liturgy - every sacred word - is sung with magnificent harmony. This is not music to get drunk by, or to teach the little children in kindergarten. The point here is that right hippocampal music appreciation includes music with distinctly spiritual connotations, so that it can recognize spiritual moods, separate from the emotions they evoke.

Verbal and non-verbal thoughts ("cognitions") are easily connected with each other, thanks in part to the structures dedicated to keeping the left and right hippocampus in touch with each other[a]. They let us connect musical intelligence and thinking with words, and vice-versa. They can also recognize when the music and music share an ethos.

The right hippocampus deals in non-verbal thinking, but it integrates spoken words easily, through its rich connections to the one on the left, so music can integrate with language, and the words of a song can match its mood. Things that can't be described can still be denoted - with the right words. Flavors and colors can have names, but you can't describe the taste of a mango. You can use words to refer to it, but they only work for people who've already tasted one.

---

[a] Such as the *dorsal hippocampal commissure*, and the *fornix commissure*, to name just two of them.

The hippocampus on the right, "thinking" without words, also plays a crucial in inner imagery[20]. This includes the images that comes to us in our dreams[21], or the images that come up when we close our eyes to try to see something in the "mind's eye"[22]. Its functions can be as mundane as closing your eyes and trying to remember what a price tag said at a local shop, but it's also working[23] when you're trying to visualize a radiant, glorious deity on a golden throne. All visual imagination, spiritual and mundane, depend on this same structure, but always working together with other brain areas. Spiritual experiences depend on ordinary brain parts, working in extraordinary ways.

It shouldn't surprise us that the hippocampus plays role in forming our memories, the most common context for inner imaging. When something happens, we experience it and then it spends a little time in short term memory and from there it's "consolidated" and made available to long term memory. The hippocampus is partly deciding what's garbage and what isn't.

How many times have you put on your shoes? The answer is, many times; sometimes several times a day. How often? How many times? We can't remember, because we do it so often. You would think that our memories of putting on our shoes would be clearer because it's been reinforced so many times, but if I asked you to remember putting on your shoes two days ago; you probably wouldn't be able to do it. Your memory system (it's actually a whole system, with the hippocampus being its most important part) would have *habituated* to the experience. You're much more likely to remember it if the shoestring snaps, because that would be a break from the routine[24].

We shouldn't assume that ordinary memory mechanisms also apply to things like past-life memories, or memories that appear through hypnotic regression[25]. Memories elicited this way can be inadvertently contrived ("confabulated") by the brain to fill in gaps created by neural issues, or to gain approval from their hypnotist[26]. Some of them may be real, but certainly not all of them. The Dalai Lama, who is famous for being the same person, life after life was once asked if he could remember his past lives. He replied: "Remember my past lives? I don't remember what I had for breakfast."

The hippocampus also plays a role in meditation. We know this from studies that found it changes through meditation[27][28]. Its role in nonverbal cognitions (nonverbal "thoughts") of space and time[29] make it the best candidate for a neural basis for thoughts about eternity and infinity (two classical attributes of God), and the other spiritual "flavors" of the right hippocampus.

My hippocampus is what tells me that one object is five or six feet from me, while another is twelve feet from me. It allows us to estimate the difference in distance[30]. Its support for spatial perception and reasoning are part of its repertoire of wordless thinking.

In one example, there was a study done in England where researchers used MRI imaging to compare the hippocampus of taxi drivers and bus drivers in London.

Parts of the hippocampus were larger in taxi drivers, who drove all over the city, than it was in bus drivers, who drove on fixed routes[31].

The hippocampus is flexible. The taxi drivers' mental map of London included the whole city, including lots of smaller streets. Maintaining a mental map of the city gave the right hippocampus so much extra work that parts of it grew in response. The hippocampus on the left is smaller in people who have been abused in childhood[32]. Sexual or physical abuse makes people more alert ("vigilant"). I think the reason may be that the left hippocampus, being connected to the left amygdala (specialized for positive emotions) has less work to do because the kid spent less time feeling good, if they can ever felt good at all. As a result, the left hippocampus had fewer jobs to do, and it atrophied.

Most religions use images of space to evoke a sense of grandeur and power, and can be invoked to create compelling images of the "end of the world".

Christianity:

> "...the stars will fall from the sky, and the heavenly bodies will be shaken." (*Gospel according to Mark*, 13:25)

> "And the heaven departed as a scroll when it is rolled together; and every mountain and island were moved out of their places." (*Revelations*, 6:14)

Islam:

When the Sky is cleft asunder;
When the Stars are scattered;
When the Oceans are suffered to burst forth;
And when the Graves are turned upside
down;-
(Then) shall each soul know what it hath sent
forward and (what it hath) kept back. (*Holy
Koran*, Sura 82 [33])

One experience that implicates the hippocampus is a common vision of an engaging, vibrant, black space. It appears in Near-Death Experiences, Peyote ceremonies, meditation, and other contexts. Often, it has a tiny point of light in the center of the person's visual field, but not always.

Here is how the Buddha described it[34]:

"There are inter-cosmic voids, an unrestrained darkness, abysmal, a pitch-black darkness, regions of blinding darkness & gloom where even the light of the sun & moon — so mighty, so powerful — doesn't reach & escape"

For those who've seen it, this space with its "blinding darkness" takes on a sacred and mysterious meaning, and even seems to be an expression of God himself.

"There is in God – Some say – a deep but dazzling darkness; as men here say it is late and dusky, because they *See* not all clear. O for that night! Where I in him might live invisible and dim!"
(Henry Vaughan (1621-1695)

Memory, the past, and the future are in the domain of the hippocampus. Memories are very easily disturbed and most of our memories actually aren't accurate. There's a game called *The Telephone game*. Science teachers used it to show how communication problems appear, and how students should ignore gossip. In this game, everyone stands in a circle. One person says something to the one next to them, and they would pass it on to the next person, through the circle, until it came out the other end. Of course, by the time it got there, the message was distorted beyond recognition.

We all do something like this with our own memories. We have an experience and when we remember it, we substitute our memory for the actual event. With time, the actual experience is at least partly disconnected from what we remember. It's common enough in courtrooms, where several people can recall the same event differently. Memories are notoriously inaccurate, and they're subject to change[35].

However, if you take what remains in memory, and talk with other people that were there for the same event about it, they'll often confirm it. The parts of our memory that are least likely to be altered are the ones where being wrong is likely to bring social consequences, like derision and ridicule. The parts of our memories that are most accurate are the ones we're most likely to talk about. We put a little extra effort into remembering things accurately when others might contradict us. However, a memory can still be distorted or partly falsified, even when others confirm it.

Let's take an example from a (male) tribal situation. After a hunt is over, a hunter might recall the day's events. Suppose they remember a buffalo coming very close to them, and *almost* threw their lance. Then, one came close enough. They threw the spear and killed the buffalo; feeding their people, especially mothers and their children, who can't hunt for themselves. The tribe appreciates this and everybody sings their name in celebration. They remember the hunt, including throwing the spear accurately, and proudly say "I threw that spear". Everyone says or sings (something like): "He is a hunter. *Our* hunter. We praise him and his skill." The people of shamanic/tribal cultures take time to praise those who do well for their people, often in front of everyone, and often through songs. "Praise singing" is a tragically lost art if there ever was one.

Remember the *attempted* kill, which the people won't put in the praise songs about them. If the hunter talks about *that* part of the hunt, the odds are good that someone will remember something different. The successful strike affects people's lives. We're a social species. Things that affect larger numbers of people need to be remembered accurately, while the memory of things that only happened to only one person can be distorted without making any trouble. Two people are more likely to remember a trivial event differently. If it's at all important, they're more likely to pay attention while it's happening, and remember it more clearly later on.

The hunter has to remember his success, which helps

people, lest he claim more skill than he actually has. He can say anything he likes about the failed attempt, which had no impact on his tribe or clan.

One of the cardinal rules in shamanic and tribal cultures is that you shouldn't take credit for things you haven't done. Like most tribal rules, It's not "official", but everyone knows that a braggart is a fool and the man or woman who brags *falsely* isn't worthy of respect. Get caught doing it, and the groups' respect can be replaced with ridicule and a touch of mistrust. This means that humans do well to exercise some self-control in the way we allow our memories to be eroded or embroidered. One of the best ways to prevent a memory from being lost or falsified is to put it in a song, story, or a new nickname for someone.

The hippocampus is deeply involved in memory. I once had a client who had memory deficits. Her brain was shaken around during a car accident. She wanted to try stimulating her hippocampus, using a method that applies a magnetic copy of an electrical signal taken from it. She applied the hippocampal signal to the left side of her brain. An excited left hippocampus can give us an unpleasant agitation, or a sense of excitement, while a busy right hippocampus helps us feel calm and relaxed[36]. In fact, the left hippocampus shows greater differences than the right[37] in schizophrenia, with its "wild and whirling words".

First, she did a session over the left side. She said that for three days she sat by a pool at a spiritual center with her mind racing, but she also said she could remember things much better. In fact, she couldn't avoid remembering things. She would have a fragmentary thought, and then it would unfold into a complete memory. A few words from a song, and the entire verse would come to mind. Her memory had improved but her thoughts were over-excited, and this is exemplifies what the left hippocampus does when it works on its own. Three days later we stimulated the right side with the same signal, which has more pleasant, silent, relaxed, and tranquil effects[38], and it all settled down. The improvements to her memory remained in place, because both the left and right hippocampus had been jolted into activity. This kind of stimulation appears to have good effects on damaged areas, as it helps reinforce the signals it uses when it's healthy.

Let me tell you about one of the most famous hippocampal case histories in the history of medicine. The treatment used in this case was only done to one person, ever. It had never been done before and it may never be done again. He was known as "Patient HM" (Henry Molaison)[39], who had seizures that originated midway down in the (limbic) temporal lobes on both sides. Not knowing what would happen, but knowing he would probably die without the surgery, they took out most of both of his hippocampuses (and most of) both amygdalas. When he awoke, he no longer had any short term memory. He forgot everything that happened within moments. Besides that, the dampening effect his two hippocampuses can have on our emotional centers seems to have been reduced.

The scientific papers about this patient are a bit dry, but there are a few TV documentaries where he can be seen for who he was. He liked everyone. He had a caretaker who would come into his room several times each day. Every time he would jump up, run across the room, and give her a hug. He didn't remember doing any of the batteries of neurological tests that he had done. A doctor might think: "Let's give him the puzzle test again, only this time let's lay out the puzzle pieces a little differently and let's see if he does it any faster or any slower." He had done it several times in the past, but of course, he didn't remember. But you could go in and say to him "Would you mind doing a test with a puzzle?" He'd say "A test with a puzzle? Great! Let's do it! OK!" Everything was fun to him.

Everything *was* fun. Everything was pleasant. Everything was novel and fresh. He'd never met anyone before, even if he'd seen them a thousand times. He kept a diary, and it had the same entry, over and over again. It said: "I've just woken up!" "I'm awake". His words seem to echo what the meditation traditions tell us: That coming to the present moment is an awakening. Patient HM had the most rare of all human experiences; a constant and undistracted access to the present moment. Losing both of his amygdala meant that the right one was gone, making it harder to fear, be anxious, or worry. Losing the left one would exclude many of the nuances for joyful moods, including enlightenment as I understand it[a], even though it looks like he had some of

---

[a] See "Sacred Pathways: The Brain's Role in Religious and Mystic

the traits of enlightened people. We can trust him to provide an example of being-here-now because we know how he got there, and because he *lived* the teaching that being in the present moment feels good. Few data sets conceal more than the data from Patient HM, which gives no clue about how much he was like a Holy Man.

It was an ultimate brain injury. The brain can accommodate injuries and the loss of faculties by redirecting the compromised function to another area of the brain. Loss of support for a skill doesn't mean that it's gone forever. People who have brain injuries usually improve for a time. They may not recover all of what they lost, but the brain recovers what it can. This was probably the case with Patient HM.

Saying yes to everything, like patient HM, is regarded as a spiritual path - all by itself. There is a movie called *The Yes Man* with Terrance Stamp. It shows an inspirational art-of-living teacher who teaches people to say yes to everything in life. It doesn't make any difference what it might be. Whatever it is, just say yes. Your life will change in no time. At least, so the film tells us. It's a great over-simplification, but there is some truth in it. I've learned that there seem to be two ways of living for ordinary people (who don't have the time and the money to see what life is like when you never say no to anything).

There seem to be two orientations. People generally say

Experiences" on Amazon.com.

no to everything unless there is a reason to say yes, or they say yes to everything unless there's a reason to say no.

The 'yesful' way of living still lets you be defensive of yourself, of course. When a man, drunk and joking, says to you "Hey. Will you give me your wallet?" you're not obliged to hand it over. There's a reason to say no, so you don't say yes. These two basic orientations of life lead to different ways of living, and different life experiences, and patient HM was better at saying *yes to everything* than anyone I've ever heard of. He had no memories to tell him what he *didn't* like doing, except memories from the time before his surgery

I had temporal lobe epilepsy as a kid and the locus (the starting point of my seizures) was probably in the right hippocampus, but very close to the fearful amygdala, its next-door neighbor, so the seizures came with an intense fear.

They also brought some powerful visual illusions. One of them is called *macropsia*[40]. It makes things look larger and farther away than they actually are. Suppose you are five feet tall and you're ten feet away from me. In this illusion, you would seem like you are five hundred feet tall and a thousand feet away. In macropsia everything seems larger and farther away, but they still *subtend* the same angle to the eye, so things *look* the same, but *feel* much bigger.

**Visual Angle Subtended
by Two Objects**

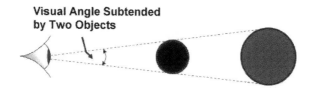

These are spatial, non-verbal illusions. The seizures were a terrifying experience for me, but not because the experience itself was frightening, but because I was in fear while it was happening; my strange macropsia. There's really nothing frightening about macropsia. In fact, there are also cases where people absolutely loved it. I *attached* my fear to it.

One early research report[41] said that one patient who had macropsia also had an illusion in which he could look at an object and it would become tremendously meaningful; "giving him great pleasure".

The spatial natures of these illusions implicate the right hippocampus[42] [43] [44], though an area that perceives space on the brain's surface also plays a role[45]. They are that heavily interconnected. For example, a seizure in this spot[a] can even damage the hippocampus[46].

There is an opposite experience. It's called *micropsia* and in this illusion, everything seems smaller. You might seem to be five inches tall and ten centimeters away from me, instead of five feet tall and ten feet away. Everything seems shrunk down. It excites the same brain parts, but in different ways.

---

[a] The occipito-temporal-parietal region, where stag deer have their antlers rooted.

Lewis Carroll, author of *Alice in Wonderland*, apparently had temporal lobe epilepsy. In fact, Macropsia and micropsia are often called "Alice in Wonderland Syndrome". Remember the words "One side makes you larger. One side makes you smaller?" Some researchers suspect that he had temporal lobe epilepsy. He had many of the personality traits that go along with temporal lobe epilepsy and that reflect a well exercised, extremely sensitive, responsive (or *labile*) hippocampus, making him very intelligent. Many of his literary motifs (travelling through a tunnel, seeing faces in flowers[a], and coherent but irrational thinking) are evocative of Temporal Lobe Epileptic experiences.

Queen Victoria read *Alice in Wonderland and through the looking-glass*. She thought it was a marvelous book. She told one of her staff to find any other books by the same author. A servant came back with the only other book Lewis Carroll had written: "*Introductory and Advanced Trigonometry*". The Queen was not amused.

I see an association between the amygdala and prayer, devotional practices, and channeling. I also see that some spiritual practices seem to recruit the hippocampus. One of them, the queen of them all, is meditation. In the Buddhist scriptures, the most important form is called V*ipassana*: "The awareness of breathing." To practice it, you remain aware (or 'mindful') of your breathing or stay conscious of any of the sensations that change in time with your breath.

---

[a] Called *pareidolia*.

You can pay attention to your breath coming in and out of your nostrils or mouth, the movement of your abdomen as you breathe, or the sensation of air going in and out of your lungs. There are many ways of paying attention to your breath, and all of them are equally acceptable. Some advanced practitioners are aware of every breath-related sensation in their entire bodies.

Because your breathing changes with each emotional state, meditation is more than just looking at your breath. You're also engaging your awareness of your emotions[a]. Not surprisingly, mindfulness meditation is gaining ground as a treatment for emotional issues[47].

For a time, I practiced meditating while was falling asleep. Remaining aware while going to sleep, prolonging the twilight state as long as you can, is an old practice. I'm not sure what tradition it's from. When you do it, you're working in the intersection of waking and sleeping, and in many shamanic traditions, that's a sacred time. Letting that awareness settle on the breath seems to be a good way to explore the twilight state. For example, visual images flashing through the mind are common in this state, and have a (you guessed it) hippocampal source[48].

Those are called *hypnagogic* phenomena and they're the product of the hippocampus on the right. You fall asleep just enough that you're no longer thinking in words, but

---

[a] To be a little more exact, we can call it the subjective experience of all emotions, no matter how subtle, in your *present* state.

awake enough that you can still think in pictures. For a while, the words stop, as the left hippocampus and the language centers on the left shut down. The right hippocampus is now busier than the one on the left, so can you find yourself seeing images in your mind, because the right hippocampus is the lord of inner imaging. I had a period in my life when I'd see breathtakingly beautiful landscapes as I fell asleep every night. You might wonder what the images mean and the answer is that they don't *mean* anything, except that you may have a more sensitive hippocampus. If it happens to you, then you probably have a good aptitude for "inner" spiritual techniques, like meditation or visualization practices. Images that have an emotional impact might have some meaning for you as private symbols, but if it's just an image; one that doesn't make you feel anything, then you won't be missing much if you don't remember it. Of course, it's another matter if you're a shaman, and you dream for your people (so to speak).

I first began spiritual practice in 1985 under a very powerful teacher, using forceful techniques that removed my head, screwed it around backwards, and put it back on again. I did five hours of yoga and meditation every day for a while and some strange things happened.

One night, just as I was falling asleep, I had a peculiar hallucination. I experienced myself in the fetal position, lying on my side. In fact, I was stretched out in my adult sleeping posture, but I felt like I was all curled up like an infant. My breath felt like I was breathing fluid instead of air. I was quick to interpret it as a return to the 'womb state'[a], breathing amniotic fluid, but the point here is that I was engrossed in the sensation of breathing. This was a body or "somatic" hallucination. There were no visible images, and no sound.

The right hippocampus seems to be specialized for pleasant expectations and the left hippocampus seems to be specialized for pessimistic ones, though the scientific literature on the subject is sparse[b]. Anger is a well-known "left hemispheric" phenomenon. Most of us are always ready to become angry or irritated if something we don't like happens, and the left hippocampus adds to the experience through its extensive connections to the left frontal lobe. This is one of the reasons why we have can have trouble finding words when we're afraid, but they flow freely when we're angry. Anger is 'hosted' on the left side, which also houses language. Fear is weighted towards the right side, away from the speech centers.

Dreams, at least the ones we remember, get their

---

[a] A state-specific somatic quasi-memory. *State-specific* because it's only available when you're in one state of consciousness. *Somatic* because it was a memory of body sensations, unconnected to any specific episode, and a *quasi-memory* because I have no actual memory to compare it to. My "remembered" womb state might really have had nothing whatsoever to do with what it felt like to be in a womb.

[b] I have heard reports of pessimism from people who have applied magnetic copies of a signal taken from the hippocampus to the left side of their heads.

imagery by exciting the right hippocampus[49]. Our dreams are woven out of images we remember, but it seems that we don't dream to enhance our memories or our memory skills[50]. In fact, they may function to help us forget things. They are a way to think using our private, personal symbolism. The right amygdala, the primary source of fear in the brain, is immediately next-door to the right hippocampus, so it's an easy matter for it to color our dreams with fear[51], making them into nightmares.

People often wake up from nightmares just before something really horrible happens. The right amygdala becomes so excited (we become so afraid) that the balance between the hippocampus and the amygdala shifts in favor of the amygdala on the right. We get really terrified and, because the right hippocampus is outmatched, the imagery stops, and we wake up. That's why we so often wake up just before horrible things actually happen in our nightmares. We've all dreamed of things which would've killed us if they'd happened in real life, but very few people dream of *really* dying.

The right amygdala becomes very busy when we have nightmares[52], especially bizarre ones[53]. It can either recruit or interfere with the excitement that's been keeping the hippocampus[a] running[54]. When the fear reaches a certain point, the imagery shuts down and we

---

[a] Note: Dreams are associated with increased hippocampal activity, but this is not the same as REM sleep. The association between the hippocampus and REM sleep is not as strong as between dreams and the hippocampus.

wake up. These two limbic structures work together intimately. One is *about* feeling and one is *about* thought. There are very few moments in life when our thoughts (verbal or non-verbal) don't initiate some kind of emotion, however trivial, and vice-versa.

Déjà Vu

Déjà vu is another hippocampal phenomenon, though it may have more than one source. It's one of the most fascinating experiences in this area of neuroscience, and there are only a few things we can do with it to help us grow spiritually. Still, everyone seems to want to know about it.

The hippocampus is where experiences in the *here and now* are prepared to become memories. There also are areas (connected to the hippocampus) on the underside of the brain's surface. This is where memory retrieval happens, and these areas are more implicated in déjà vu than the hippocampus itself.

In fact, memories aren't "stored" in the brain. Science is still arguing with itself over what memories are "made of", but there is some agreement that memories aren't 'written' to the brain like information on a hard drive[55]. Pulling up old memories and rendering new ones don't involve anything like computer RAM[a]. We use the

---

[a] Computer RAM has been used as a metaphor for short-term memory. It stands for *Random Access Memory*, so that memory has been used as a metaphor for RAM, while RAM is used as a metaphor

metaphors anyway, because we don't have any better ones right now. In time, a student will find a better model, their professor will reject their work, and then they'll publish anyway. And change the world of cognitive science forever.

Long-term memory is grounded in the parahippocampal cortex, which consists of the parahippocampal gyrus, the entorhinal cortex, and a couple of others.

Déjà vu seems to happen when the hippocampus is overly-connected to the hippocampal cortex. The area that's involved with perceiving the present[56] is overly-connected to the areas that work to remember the past. This means your mind is trying to recall the past at the same time it remembers the present, making the here and now *feel* like a moment from the past.

Hyper-connectivity between neighboring brain parts is common in some psychiatric disorders, people who are sensitive to altered-states (especially the spiritual ones), and epilepsy[57], which is why people with these issues are prone to déjà vu.

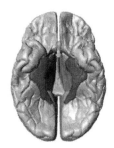

The hippocampal cortex, as seen from below. It's the main source for Déjà vu.

One explanation says that 'a

for memory. It's a piece of circular reasoning.

transfer of familiarity' fails. This theory tells us that when your brain tries to apply a memory of a past situation to your current one, fails, and makes the present feel more familiar than it should. This implies that déjà vu is an odd instance of memory at work. I think it's much more likely to be an unusual perception of the *present*, not the past, and indeed, these some of these theories are based on studying déjà vu in epileptics with memory problems[58], not ordinary people. Being reminded of something, but also being unable to recall what it was might trigger déjà vu, but that doesn't explain why it always feels so meaningful, and why if feels different from just failing to remember something. In other words, déjà vu isn't like forgetting where you put your keys.

In my view, déjà vu appears when there are too many connections between the present (in short-term memory), and the past (in long-term memory), so the present *feels* like a moment from the past, coming back once again[59].

It can be triggered by a brain "glitch", when we feel that something is familiar, but can't recall where we know it from. In that moment, the *present* act of remembering fails to connect with anything from the *past*. Another possibility is that we are reminded of too many things at once when we attempting to remember something, and can't find the memory we're looking for.

In déjà vu, you aren't living a moment recurring from the past, but the present moment feels so 'past like' or is so imbued with "past-ness", that you naturally think it's a past moment returning in the present.

The hippocampus (and the nearby areas on the brain's surface) is so adroit at handling images and context that it's been called the brain's *contextualization engine*. It can literally create a false memory[60] or embroider (*confabulate*) a real memory to match a moment of déjà vu. You might remember a moment in the past that the déjà vu evokes, but it could be a completely fabricated, counterfeit, or a memory that's been adapted to match the present, without your ever knowing it. As we might expect, people who have déjà vu frequently are also prone to false memories[61].

Unlike memories of the past, the present is unyielding and uncompromising. You can't *make* it change by wanting it to change. You can change your interpretation of it, but you can't change *it*. I can't use my "will" so that I'm writing this book in the Taj Mahal. It's beyond my power. I can make it seem more fun than it is with the right attitude or I can make it seem like a burden, but I can't make it happen anywhere but *here* and *now*.

It's a *lot* easier for the brain to create a false memory than it is to falsify (or hallucinate) events in the present.

It's possible that déjà vu could involve an event in the present evoking a specific memory in the past, but more likely, all it takes is an out-of-place *sense* of the past to trigger déjà vu in the present, a sense than runs amok when it fails to find out why something is familiar, and the memory system fails for a moment. There is a *sense* of the past. It's the sense that tells you whether something happened yesterday, or many weeks ago, *before* you fully remember it. "Long ago" feels different from "last week", and there is a subtle sense that knows that difference[62].

Déjà vu has an opposite. Just as the present can be hyper-connected to the past in our brain, it's also possible to disconnect the present from the past so radically that nothing in the present is familiar. If you look in a mirror in such moments, the face you find there is completely unknown to you.

It's called *jamais vu*. Déjà Vu means 'ever seen'. Déjà is 'ever' and Vu is 'seen'. Jamais vu means 'never seen'. During Jamais Vu, nothing in the present moment matchs anything from the past, and this can make ordinary experiences become very, very strange. It's not well known, and it doesn't happen anywhere near as often. Jamais vu can happen when the hippocampus and the nearby hippocampal cortex are relatively disconnected.

Most of the experiences that come from epilepsy, brain injury, or chemical "insults" to the brain, involve *disinhibition*. In other words, they make the brain more sensitive. What seems to drive all of these experiences – sacred and profane, spiritual or pathological – is extra connectivity between its parts. When two areas are more connected than usual, even temporarily, these areas will create experiences, as '*mental forms follow neural functions*'. Any change in brain activity, whether it's ordinary, spiritual or pathological, is going to create a change in state of consciousness.

The question appears: what can you do when you get déjà vu? How can you use it spiritually? First of all, there are no mental tricks to *make* it happen. Instead, you have to wait for it to happen on its own. When *this* moment feels like a return of a past moment, there's a tendency to want to recall the past moment you're 'deja-vu-ing' to. My advice is - *don't*.

Don't try to remember the past moment it may have come from. Forget it. It's a dead end. Millions of people through history have had déjà vu and tried to remember where the feeling came from, and nothing came of it. They wonder about this strange feeling, asking: *What is this?,* but the answer hasn't been forthcoming.

When you have déjà vu, be *present*. Deny yourself permission to remember the past. Be wholly and completely in-the-now. When you refuse to go into the past, and avoid activating your memories, where will the focus for that neurological energy end up? Back in the place that's most sensitive at that moment; in and around the hippocampus. Remember it turns our *present* experience into memories, which is to say it's concerned with *this moment.* Now; even as it handles the past.

When you have a moment of Déjà Vu, don't search your mind looking for a corresponding moment in the past. Just be present. What does it feel like to have *now* feel like *then*? What does "*pastness*" feel like? With that inquiry, you can deepen your experience of the present moment and that, in turn, can contribute to any practice that emphasizes the present, most importantly, meditation.

We might say that déjà vu is meditation's way of coming to get you, but we almost always grab it by the wrong end, instinctively trying to remember something from the past. Instead, grab it by the *present*. If the experience is strong enough, a few of the synapses that normally hold us back us from remembering the present can drop out, letting you get there more easily. Processing it makes a good lead baseball bat for meditation.

Have you watched baseball players warming up to take the bat? They'll work out for a moment beforehand; with a bat made of lead. Afterwards, when they pick up the wooden bat, it feels like it weighs nothing. In the same way, staying aware of the present moment during a moment of déjà vu, can make "staying present" in more ordinary moments seem easy.

Do This:

If you can, stop what you're doing when you have déjà vu, and go into meditation *right then*. Be mindful of the present just when your mind is calling you to wonder about the past.

The challenge with déjà vu is the same as the challenge in meditation. Forget the past, including the past that only happened two minutes ago, and pay attention to your experience this instant. That's how to use déjà vu. If you get it a lot, great. If you don't get it so often, wonderful. If you don't know what it feels like, marvelous.

The "Open Space" imaginative exercise.

Now we come to our next exercise, which works with our sense of space. As I mentioned before, the hippocampus is instrumental in spatial perceptions and spatial reasoning, like judging how far things are from us, or measuring distances mentally. For example, you know how many hundreds of yards something is by imagining how many football fields they are from you. The hippocampus maintains our "mental maps", helping us navigate from our homes to the nearest food store, our way to work, and all the other routes we use to get ourselves around.

These exercises work best at night, when melatonin levels in the brain are rising. For this exercise, you should first take a moment and put yourself into some kind of trance. Any sort will do. Then, with your eyes closed, imagine that there is an empty space behind you, but only on your *left*. Then, imagine that the space is behind you and on your *right*.

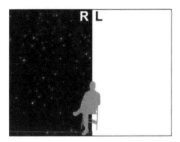

This exercise consists of imagining space behind you on both sides, one side at a time. Your left is the figure's right, and vice-versa.

Did you notice a difference in the quality, tone or texture of the space on the left and on the right? Most people who can evoke a sense of space this way feel that the two sides each have their own personality or "feel".

The response is different because the hippocampus on the right is much more involved in spatial perception than the one on the left. When we imagine space on our right, the right hippocampus responds easily. It offers a good preparation for meditation. When you first sit down to meditate, imagine a space behind you and on your right for a minute and then begin. Use it to *enhance* your meditation, not replace it.

It can also be useful for disconnecting from emotions. The different functions of the hippocampus and the amygdala reflect the differences between thoughts and feelings. Being "in" one pushes you away from the other. This exercise seems to 'downshift' the amygdala allowing more thought (including the silent thoughts meditation[63] works with), and less emotion, making it easier to reach towards a sense of equanimity, detachment or dispassion. But – and this is a big "but" – the moments when we're the most emotional are also the times when it's hardest to do. With practice, you'll know when you can use it and when you can't.

Just like the sensed presence imagination, some people have very strong responses to it and others have little or none, because some people's hippocampus are more responsive than others. It may easier if you do it when you're a little tired than when you're active and energized. A touch of fatigue can work as a *control mechanism* from another structure, the *caudate nucleus*.

The Caudate Nucleus (who we'll meet in our next

chapter) on the right seems specialized for relaxation, and its counterpart on the left appears to support arousal; feeling active, alert, and energetic, focused, and present for the things going on around you. The time of day when you do the 'open space' exercise makes a difference, too. You have a better chance of activating the right hippocampus with this exercise at night, when you're more relaxed.

Perhaps you remember learning in a high school science class that the left side of the brain controls the right side of the body. When you are working with your imagination, the right side of the body is connected to the right side of the brain and the left is connected to the left. However, we're talking *imagination* here, so the wiring is a bit different. If we were trying to evoke a hallucination, then the sides would switch, and the normal neural wiring you learned in a science class, would come into play[64].

As you may have noticed already, the hippocampus supports a wide range of phenomenon. This is because it's a cognitive, 'thinking' structure, and we have many different ways of thinking. The amygdala, which we talked about earlier, is much more emotional, and its functions are less complicated. We have more ways of thinking than we have ways of feeling. Even though the nuances of our emotions are incredibly subtle, we see fewer themes in the amygdala than we do in the hippocampus.

Out OF Body Experiences

One of the most fascinating hippocampal phenomena is out-of-body experiences ("OBEs"). The hippocampus helps us see where things are, including ourselves, in space. There is evidence that the hippocampus plays a role in these intriguing experiences[65]. In OBEs, we feel as though our awareness and our bodies are in different places. Perhaps we actually *are* out of our bodies, so that the center of consciousness has left the brain and it's now located outside us. Perhaps we're having a hallucination of our actual environment, but from a different perspective. The hippocampus is involved in both creating our memories and in spatial perception, so it's easy for memories and space to get mixed up, or more accurately, to have both working at once, when their underlying brain areas are both either too active, or not active enough. In this way, we could *hallucinate* the space around us, seeing it from another perspective, and the subjective experience is one of an OBE.

There are many spiritual teachers, especially from the Hindu tradition, who tell us that the whole world is just an illusion. If the space that we are in now is an illusion, then when we go out of our body in an OBE, we're creating the world around us just as much as when we're in our bodies. If you believe that "all is illusion", then the experience of an OBE is illusory whether you're "really" out of your body or not. A question appears; are OBEs real (meaning that "you" are no longer in your body) or are they hallucinatory (meaning that you remain in your body, and you're "just" seeing the world from another angle)?

I'm reminded of a bit of dialog from the Harry Potter films:

> Question: "Is this real or is it happening in my head"?
> Answer: "Why should it being in your head mean it's not real"?

There is no compelling evidence that *proves* OBEs are either "real" or hallucinations. Many people have had out of body experiences during near death experiences (NDEs) and in a few cases, people came back to life remembering their OBE, but their memories didn't match the actual location exactly. Of course, the discrepancy may have to do with a flawed memory of the event, or it may be that the event wasn't "really real". One case involved someone who had an out of body experience in which he looked down on the scene and saw what was going on there. Everything he saw was quite accurate, except that there were two more people in the actual scene than he remembered from his OBE. It's also possible that he really was out of his body, but his memories about it were flawed.

Our feelings are somewhat muted when the hippocampus is very active[a]. We're less emotional and more able to create accurate memories when we don't get excited about what we perceive. The more thoughtful or rational we are, the less emotional. It can be difficult to play a good game of chess when we're

---

[a] The role of the hippocampus in reducing emotional responses is not well-studied in the normal population. Most studies on the subject are concerned with schizophrenia.

feeling fearful or joyous.

Some people make mistakes in remembering the details of an out of body experience, and that tends to suggest that not everything we remember about being out of our bodies is objectively true or that OBE memories are accurate. Some of it was created in our minds, and there are no tests that will prove what is and what isn't "real". Some researchers have suggested that we should put markers in emergency rooms that could only be seen from an out-of-body perspective (typically above the patient). I doubt many people would care about such details while they were waiting to see whether or not they would die. Although personal experience is never really scientific evidence, I'll say that I've had OBEs, and I very much doubt that I would have bothered to notice a visual cue small enough to be hidden from people on the floor. I was only interested in what was happening to *me*.

Out of body experiences are difficult to study scientifically, especially if the research is limited to standard scientific methods. You might do an EEG or a PET scan on the person. But then they'd be stuck in a large tube that scans their body, or have a complicated array of wires attached to their head, which isn't very relaxing. The circumstances would be very different from the ones in which out of body experiences happen naturally. The sterile context and the 'demand' that they have an OBE can both make them less likely or even change the experience.

All the OBE teachers I've read say about the same thing.

People should *allow* OBEs to happen, and not try to *force* them. Scientists can study it in context and wait for the evidence to appear, or they can study it out of context in laboratories and gather evidence that may not pertain to what most OBEers (out of body experiencers) actually go through. There are lots of researchers who want to either prove or debunk OBEs, but few who want to understand the subjective experience.

There is a concept in quantum mechanics called *The Uncertainty Principle*. It says that you can measure the position of an electron but not its speed, or you can measure the speed but not its position. Observing the electron means using some kind of input (like particles of light) to make the observation (which happens when the light bounces back out). The problem is that the stream of light (photons) carries enough energy to deflect the electrons it's supposed to observe. Watching the phenomena changes it.

Similarly, we know a lot about what's happening in someone's brain while they're having an OBE[a] because people who can do it at will have been studied, and we can study how OBEs occur and what types of things are commonly reported *when they happen naturally*, but science can't seem to do both at once. And that's perfectly alright with me. I like science to be rigorous and exact, but sometimes it should be left a bit fuzzy around the edges, especially when there is disagreement about something. We are simply not at the point to

---

[a] OBEs are most often associated with changes in the temporo-parietal junction, an area about 2.5 inches above the ears.

where we can put all the evidence about OBEs together into a single explanation. The scientific community and spiritual seekers who have some faith in science shouldn't expect that everything will always be perfectly consistent.

How to (try to) have OBEs

There is a technique for having out of body experiences. I'll explain it to you now, but don't to try it while reading this book.

There are a few situations where OBEs happen quite often, like near-death experiences, and drug induced hallucinations, but most spontaneous out of body experiences happen while people are in bed, falling to sleep. OBEs relate to our sense of our position in space, via the hippocampus, working together around a place on the surface of the brain called the *angular gyrus*.

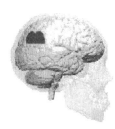

The Angular Gyrus.

A Swedish researcher, Olaf Blanke, stimulated the angular gyrus of an epileptic woman, and immediately elicited an out of body experience[66].

The OBE stopped when he took the electrode away. He did it again in the same place, and the patient had another one.

The media promptly announced it as the discovery of a center in the brain for out of body experiences. Then, just as quickly, the press forgot about it. Eventually, the scientific community said (or seemed to say – science never speaks with one voice) "Wait a minute. Other areas are involved, too." Naturally, the media took no notice.

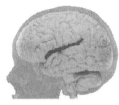

The Sylvian Fissure.

One of these areas is called the *Sylvian Fissure.* It separates the temporal lobes from the rest of the brain. Stimulation of this area on the right side elicited out of out of body experiences in the 1950s. In 2010, an experiment created an OBE in a normal subject by using magnetic fields that circled around the head[67]. One case history was published that used brain imaging during an OBE in a person who could have such experiences at will[68], a rare talent. All of these cases implicated different brain areas. At first, it looked simple and now it looks complicated again. Different studies shows different areas at work in OBEs, but it seems that there is no single brain center for OBEs, The neural processes that create them are still not fully understood[a], but it seems to be a process involving many areas.

The Balance System

Most people (80%, according to an online poll) have felt sensations of movement when they're actually keeping

---

[a] I'm in the "interhemispheric intrusion" school of thought. This hypothesis says that such dramatic events originate from sudden intense bursts of activity across the brain, exciting ordinary brain parts in extraordinary ways.

still. It can appear in several ways. One of the most common is the feeling we get when we see a video taken from the front of a roller coaster in television ads for theme parks. You can actually feel like you're moving just by seeing a video filmed with a moving camera. There is another one, and it offers a starting point for people who want to have OBEs. I'm talking about the feeling your that the bed is moving while you're dropping off to sleep. For some, it may be a rocking sensation. For others, it can be the feeling that the bed is rising, falling or spinning.

Such sensations come from the *vestibular* sense (or the *vestibular system*), which tells us where we're located in space. Its best-known disturbance is *vertigo*: "a sensation of whirling or loss of balance commonly associated with looking down from a great height".

The way to work towards having out of body experience is to try to imagine sensations of movement deliberately, and the best time for that's when you're falling asleep.

The OBE Exercise

The technique for having an out of body experience is to lie in bed and imagine a sensation of movement, and allow or invite that imagination to unfold into a real sensation, especially rocking with your head and feet going up and down. Lots of people can induce the sense of movement just through imagination though it may take a bit of practice. Don't expect it to happen the first time you try it. You chances are much better if you've had such sensations in the past.

You imagine/remember the sense of movement until the feeling really appears. Once that's happened, you relax as much as you can. Trying *harder* won't help. The trick is be relaxed while feeling the sense of movement. One key seems to be *disconnecting* from anything that distracts you from that sensation. Another is not trying to force it to appear. Eventually, you can simply rotate or roll yourself out of your body. It's actually a common OBE induction technique, but only when it's practiced regularly. The difficult part is creating the sensation of mild movement in the first place. Not everyone is prone to it, or even knows what it feels like. Staying relaxed when it starts to work is s a second challenge

Psychic Perceptions

As we mentioned before, the right hippocampus is involved in inner imaging – "metal pictures". If you know the mind's eye's repertoire, you'll naturally wonder 'What about psychic perception?' There is evidence that people who report psychic experiences have a more active right hippocampus than those who don't[69].

It's difficult for science to study psychic perceptions *per se*. Many scientists are closed minded about them, but there have been a few (including my mentor, Dr. Michael Persinger) who studied both the *propensity* to report them, as well as also demonstrating quantifiable psychic perceptions. He put the focus of his studies on *reports* of psychic experiences instead of the perceptions themselves, and that led to a few breakthroughs[a]. No one can argue that some people are more likely to report psychic perceptions than others, or that the people who do have unique personalities. Few skeptics will argue that these traits shouldn't be studied.

Becoming Psychic

There is a way of developing psychic perceptions, but it's a less specific technique than our other exercises. It consists of paying ever closer attention to your *first* inner responses to ordinary things, without trying to pick out the psychic ones.

A fascination with perception itself is more helpful for developing psychic skills than wanting to engage the 'special', telepathic, clairvoyant, or remote-viewing ones. Being interested in empathy won't help you become an empath. A real interest in other people will help you far more.

The way to become psychic (if you have the aptitude for it) is to pay attention to your mind's responses to events of any kind. Anything you see, hear, feel, think or perceive[b], in any way, will trigger a response, however

---

[a] These experiments are discussed in my other book, "Sacred Pathways: the brain's role in religious and mystic experiences."

[b] A more technical way of putting it would be to use a phrase that encompasses all perceptions, thoughts, and emotions in one concept. I've used the phrase "sensory, cognitive and affective modalities" to denote this in other writings. It's not unlike the Buddhist concept of *mental factors* (Sanskrit: *caitasika*; Pali: *cetasika*; Tibetan: *sems byung*). In Buddhism, these are identified as

brief or subtle. Let me emphasize that this includes our own thoughts. For example, something might remind you of someone you know, and the very next thing that appears in your mind may be a psychic insight about them. It happens fast, and it's easy to miss them when you don't know what you're looking for.

Much of the time, our minds respond to events with meaningless trivia, but our immediate, instant responses are often giving us information that's relevant in that moment – without using words. Being a linguistic species, many of us are so involved with our own inner monolog that we aren't available to notice our non-verbal thoughts. Even the most sensitive psychics don't notice their own wordless responses all the time.

I doubt that psychic skills are unique to humans. There are huge numbers of stories of animal psychic skills. Dogs often seem to know when their owners are coming home, though skeptics reject the proof[70]. I suspect that psychic perceptions are one of the mental skills remaining from our evolutionary ancestors; from the time before we acquired language. Speech and linguistic thinking may have replaced other kinds of thought. Our psychic "reasoning" may have been replaced with our own verbal thoughts, including *prosody*, the "felt"

---

subjective events in the mind that apprehend the quality of an object, and that have the ability to "color" the mind. Mental factors are categorized as formations (Sanskrit: *sankhāra*) concurrent with mind (Sanskrit: *citta*). Alternate translations for mental factors include "mental states", "mental formations" "mental events", and "concomitants of consciousness". In my school of thought, we refer to the "present content of consciousness".

aspects of language. Everything that happens inspires us to think of things to say. We often know our own responses to events through the words they bring to mind instead of the more direct, (but much less social) images that appear in our mind's eye, ("visual thinking"). The pictures in our heads are much easier to share with others psychically than our words are, but only when the words or emotions in our mind don't get in the way, and that's almost all the time. You have to quiet things down to be telepathic, and that's why so many psychics put themselves in a trance or a reverie when they want to 'read' something.

This brings us to another psychic technique.

Caveat: How to "talk" to animals.

Talking to animals involves a very simple technique. Look at the animal, think in pictures, and let your emotions come as strongly as possible. If you want keep your dog to stop soiling your floor, look at the dog, feel anger, and picture the mess they made in your mind. If you want to call your cat to you to cuddle with it, look at the cat, find a loving mood, and imagine the cat in your arms. Of course, cats aren't very obedient, so the more aloof your cat is, the less chance they will respond. Lots of things can influence the rapport people can have with their pets and work animals, and they affect our psychic connections with them. Like all the techniques in this book, not everyone will have the same success.

The first thing that comes up in your mind in response to an event, a statement, a picture, some news, one of your own thoughts, a flash of emotion - whatever it is - will often be a psychic perception, but they come and go quickly, and can be rapidly replaced by our own inner dialogue, and our thoughts, impressions and emotional responses. We're so dependent on language that we tend to replace everything that happens in our minds with words that help us tell others about it – automatically. There is even evidence that pictures get us ready ("prime" us) to use words much more easily than the other way around[71].

Most of the time, we don't respond to events at all. Instead, we react to our own inner dialog about them. To a large extent, becoming psychic simply means paying attention to the images, words and sensations that your mind creates as its *immediate* response to things. However, the gap between an event and your *instant* response to it can be so short, and the tendency to respond with emotions or words can be so strong that the first *cognitive* response (with some information) can be almost completely washed out.

There is an adage in the Samurai arts. It says "meet your opponent's sword as the spark flies from the steel." A good swordsman will respond to their opponent's moves instantly, before they know they're doing it. That's how immediately your brain can produce a response to something, and that's how fast a psychic perception can be.

There are powerful psychics, like Ingo Swann, the remote viewer. There are also honest spiritual teachers who use their empathetic skills to help their students.

They're not so different from ordinary people. They're just capable of noticing their immediate responses to things, and they don't respond to events with mind chatter. The take notice of what appears in their minds, and they don't start interpreting it until after they've had a good look at it. They won't ask where it came from or what it means. They just spend a few extra milliseconds focused on the perception, seeing it clearly, before thinking about what it means.

Based on what I know about how the brain works, the amount of time your brain takes for its immediate responses is between 25 and 400 milliseconds (some are faster than others). 400 milliseconds is almost half a second. If you are a musician, and you're playing a rhythm with beats coming at slightly less than half a second, then a quarter of a second is a long time. If you are playing a melody and the drum misses the beat by a quarter of a second (by 250 milliseconds), you'll notice it. You might even get irritated at the drummer. When I say between 25 and 400 milliseconds, it sounds really, really fast, but it's not outside the realm of our normal responses. If a video's sound is out of synch by just a few milliseconds you'll notice it, which shows just how fast our ordinary perceptions can be.

Why can we respond to some things in such a short amount of time and not others? It's simply that the things we respond to most quickly usually *mean* something to us. They create emotional responses, and emotions tend to disperse many kinds of thought, and psychic impressions are one of them. The raw information from the hippocampus and surrounding areas is routed to other areas, mixing it with our emotions. However, this doesn't mean that psychics aren't very emotional. Some of them are very sensitive, but they have a knack for perceiving things without instantly becoming emotional. A negative image in their minds won't spark fear as quickly as it would for others. It takes them just a little longer to become angry, or to assume that their desires will be fulfilled by what they see. The difference may be only in milliseconds, but that can be a long time for the brain.

When you have a psychic perception, what you perceive may not mean anything to you. At other times, it will spark an emotional response, and that takes the focus of activity from our friend, the right hippocampus and moves it to the amygdala. If it's a positive response, it will reach across the brain to add a positive tone, courtesy of the left amygdala. If it's a negative one, the right hippocampus can recruit the right amygdala, its immediate next-door neighbor, adding a fearful touch. Negative psychic perceptions have more survival value (by alerting us to threats), and the brain's architecture makes them much easier to provoke. It also explains one of my own observations about psychics, that they are usually more likely to give warnings than encouragement. The pathways between psychic perceptions and response to threats, involving two structures, immediately next to each other, are much shorter than those between psychic awareness and potential opportunities, which run across the brain to the other side. Bad news appears more quickly than good news.

If you ever choose to work with a psychic, ask them if they see more threats or more opportunities in their work. If they usually give their clients warnings, then they may be powerless to see anything that's good for you. If you're hoping for good news, then don't work with them. Instead, find a psychic with an equal ability to foresee both good news and bad. This usually means a psychic who does spiritual work, like intensive prayer, meditation, spiritual rituals, yoga, etc. These practices help keep them in a positive frame of mind. If they don't keep their own positive emotions available, they often won't be able to see anything positive for you. Frightened clients are more likely to come back for more advice – and pay for it. Be careful. Seeing a psychic that who only gives you warnings can be bad for your mental health.

There are many spiritual teachers say that anyone can be psychic. This may be true, but not everyone has to overcome the same obstacles to getting psychic responses. People with busy minds will have a harder time. The content of our minds changes very quickly. Most of the things we respond to with psychic perceptions don't mean anything to us and it takes a very rare psychic to be able to accurately predict the outcome of something that scares them or fills them with desire. Fear of bad outcomes - and the desire for good ones – are strong distractions. "All is clouded by desire: as fire by smoke, as a mirror by dust, as an unborn babe by its covering[a]."

Fear of negative perceptions and being greedy for the positive ones disrupts psychic perception. That's why psychics are often unable to do readings for themselves. They care too much. Suppose your child goes missing, and you visit a remote viewer to try to find out where they are. The Remote Viewer should be able to clear their mind long enough to look for them. If it's *their* kid, then they will probably be so upset that they'll have trouble locating them. Their own hopes and fears will get in the way.

The process of becoming psychic includes building equanimity, dispassion and a healthy detachment. The first time you have one such perception come to you, spontaneously and unbidden, you *recognize* it as a psychic perception and you also *confirm* it's accuracy, from then on you'll know what you're looking for. The first psychic perception is the one that takes the most patience. Another part of the process is confirming your perceptions. You *must* test yourself. It can be embarrassing, and it doesn't feel so good when you find that you're wrong, but there is no substitute for it.

Your brain's reward system will motivate you to notice when you're right, and when you're wrong. It will react when psychic perceptions are on the mark, and when they're not. If you put your self-esteem on the line after you "see" something psychically, and it doesn't work

---

[a] Bhagavad Gita: 3, 38

out, you'll know not to follow "*that*" feeling. When it works out well, and your insight is confirmed, you'll feel good, and your brain's reward system will help you learn that you *should* follow "*this*" feeling. You have to take small risks to find out if your inner images hold psychic information, or you'll never learn the "gut feeling" that tells you when you're probably right. Authors have to seek out critics to help them refine their writing. Artists have to see people responding to their work. Scientists have to look at their data to see how well their experiments match their expectations. Children have to learn which of their actions bring approval or punishment. *All* skills need to be checked and refined over time, and the psychic ones are no exception.

My first truly clear psychic perception appeared to me at a time when I was doing a lot of meditation. Meditation involves non-verbal information processing, so I was primed for it. I had gone to see a friend of mine who had just moved into a new home, and she said to me "This place is perfect. I *manifested* it. I put my will out to the universe to bring me the perfect home, and this is what it gave me. It's perfect in every way except one … and I shouldn't say that it isn't perfect in any way. It's just absolutely perfect."

She wanted to be grateful to the universe in all she did. Sometimes it's a great theme, but not so good at other times. There are no positive thoughts or attitudes that work for *every* circumstance. Finding a 100 dollar bill on the street will never create the same state of consciousness as being told you need surgery. One hurts, and the other feels good. Being grateful for pain may be the mark of an advanced spirituality, but it can also be a sign of destructive mental habits.

You can force your thoughts to make negative events seem positive, but to the natural mind, an untrained mind, the organic mind, good things are good and bad things are bad.

She said: "There's one thing missing ..." from her perfect home, and as soon as she said that, before she could correct her words to bring them in line with her belief that everything should inspire gratitude, I had a 'flash' of fireworks in my mind. I said "Well, what about fireworks?"

Surprised, she replied, "How could you know that?" No, she didn't actually shoot off fireworks. She explained that she had built a brick fireplace outside her last home. It was modeled on the kind used in Hindu fire ceremonies[a]. She said she would sit, make a fire, and wait till it burned down to coals, and then she would throw bath salts into the flames, creating little flames in different colors. She did this as a private devotional practice. Sounds lovely. That was the moment when I knew what psychic perceptions were.

The image came as an instant "flash", and I was confused, wondering how it could be fireworks when they're illegal in her state? *How could fireworks be the*

---

[a] Agni Puja. Agni is the Hindu God of Fire, who accepts offerings on behalf of other gods and goddesses.

only thing that she was missing? It confused me enough that I stayed with it a bit longer than an ordinary passing thought. I attended or *adverted* to the image, and then I confirmed it, or rather, she confirmed it for me.

The word *advert* is more common in Buddhist psychology than in other places. *Adverting* to something means to let it take your attention. *Advert*ising catches our attention and focuses it on something. Pictures of women with deep cleavages holding beer cans in front of expensive cars advertise things to "typical" men. It can sell either the beer or the car.

It catches our attention and holds it. Perhaps not for very long, but it grabs and holds. That's what you want to do with imagery, sounds, flashes of music, even smells, that come up instantly in response to whatever happens. We could say that psychic perceptions are advertisements from our subconscious. Pay attention to them. Keep them in your mind long enough to see them clearly. Some psychics put themselves in a mild trance (another item on the hippocampus' menu[72]), and wait for a psychic impression, contemplating whatever they're trying to *see*. They create an inner environment that invites these flashes of insight, and then just wait for something to appear. Both the trance and the inner images have their foundations in the hippocampus.

The trick is to be quick with your attention. Don't move on from those inner perceptions. Don't explore your reactions to them. Don't push them away when they're unpleasant. Sometimes they *are* negative, and that's one of the reasons why I don't want to be an accomplished psychic[a].

Most people build up psychic skills and intuitions in response to the tasks and circumstances they meet regularly. You may have had a job where you could tell what mood your boss was in with just a brief glance. That can be all it takes to know that this is not a good day to ask for a raise, or you know that this isn't the time to tell them that an invoice had a mistake. Another day, they come in to work in a different mood, and you'll see that now is the time. You don't need to study their face in order to do it. You look at your boss, and you just know. The line between intuition and psychic impressions is very blurry.

A mother can tell what her infant wants by the tone of its cry. It often it conveys more than just a tone of voice would. With such intimate bonds, the line between intuitive and psychic is easy to cross. There probably isn't any such border; I expect it will turn out to be a fuzzy area where they overlap and flow into each other.

We may not always recognize psychic perceptions when

---

[a] There are cynics, hecklers, and skeptics who may throw some faulty logic at you, demanding that you prove that psychic perceptions are "real" by telling them who will win a sports event, or an election, or demand winning lottery numbers. Such folly ignores the facts. 1) Most psychic perceptions are spontaneous and don't appear on demand. 2) Most psychic insights are about individual people. 3) Not everyone who has the capacity for psychic knowledge wants to make it a priority in their lives. 4) People who aren't psychic don't have the experience to tell an easy psychic perception from one that's almost impossible. 5) Not all psychics are equally skilled. 6) Some psychics *practice* more than others.

they appear. I'd like to have empathetic skills; the psychic ability to work with people; looking at them and seeing what's happening in their lives. I have no interest in learning remote viewing, for example. I can often talk to people, notice their tone of voice, seen their body language, and tell which of the brain structures we've been talking about in this book is most excitable for that person. I can use a few questionnaires to check to see if I'm right, and I usually am. My work in the area has honed my perception to the point where I don't know if it's psychic, intuitive or an insight. And I don't care. I don't do it to become psychic. I do it as part of my work. My commitment is to my vocation, not the skills it uses. If I'm empathetic in this area, it comes from developing my work as much as psychic awareness. But then, how could I be sure? I'm looking at *people*, not my own mind.

Psychic skills depend on having a well-exercised hippocampus on the right side, so all of the exercises that work with it, (including the "open space" imagination we discussed before) can help, but the most important technique for developing psychic skills is simply being as aware as you can of what happens in your mind, from one second to the next. Meditation trains people to be aware of inner events, so it's good exercise for developing psychic impressions, though any meditation teacher will tell you that isn't one of its usual goals. Meditation builds awareness, but it's only one of the many facets of the psychic arts.

Opening the Third Eye

There are several traditions that tell us that the third eye is the "home" of psychic skills. We find this idea in Hinduism, with its teachings on Kundalini and the chakras, theosophy and "new age" teachings, to name only three. Sometimes, it seems like everyone wants to "open their third eye". Many teachings on the subject seem a bit misguided. I won't say that any of the older instructions for accessing the third eye are wrong. I'll just say that the one we'll talk about here is so easy that you should try it.

The third eye is more of a *metaphor* than an organ of sight. The traditional teaching tells us to roll our eyes upward and gaze at the spot between our eyebrows. I tried this technique for years, pointing my eyes upwards, towards the spot between my eyebrows. In the end, a much simpler and less strenuous technique worked better for me. I've asked many people to test it. It worked for most of them, and it led me to a new understanding of what the third eye is.

Let me be clear: "third eye" is a *good* metaphor. I won't try to give it a new and better name. The third eye *is* analogous to an eye. You may have seen pictures of ultra holy, über-Yogis, sitting in the Himalayas with their hands in special poses ("Mudras") and their eyes rolled up in their heads. Something is wrong with these images. They're not looking *through* their third eye. They're looking *at* it. The reason it's the *third* eye is, well … because it isn't the first two.

We don't look at our own eyes. We don't taste our own tongues. We don't smell our own noses. Or senses are not for perceiving themselves. They're for apprehending the world around us. If you want to see someone's aura or read their emotional state psychically, do you use your eyes to look at your third eye? No, and you don't use one eye to look at the other. You use them both to look *outward*, at the person in front of you.

A question appears: what does an "open third eye" mean? To answer it, we'll do another of our brief exercises.

The "Third Eye Exercise"

As before, it begins with closing your eyes. Give yourself a moment to go into a light trance. Next, point your eyes downward just a little bit, and at the same time, be *aware* of the upper section of your field of vision. The idea is to point your eyes downward while your vision gazes upward. If you do this often enough, you'll "get it", and you'll know it, though you should expect to put in some effort. It may start as a sensation that your 'inner vision' has become richer, deeper or taken on a non-visual quality, like a little bit of synesthesia. You may *feel* the blank and black visual field in your body. You might have an urge to cross your eyes. Give in to that urge, but don't strain.

When you move your focus away from where your eyes are pointing, you allow your visual attention to separate from your sight, making it more available for images from within, through the right hippocampus, so it can add its pictorial information to your visual attention. The name "second sight" makes sense. The right hippocampus is responsible for inner imaging of any kind, including the psychic variety. You become a *seer* when you see images that relate to the people around you.

This kind of visual "tasking" doesn't happen in our normal daily lives. We don't separate our visual attention from our eyes naturally when we're awake, but there is one ordinary state where it can happen spontaneously; as we're falling asleep and we shut down our normal vision. The most common natural context for it is in the gap between waking and sleeping; the twilight state. For normal minds and brains, it may be the only context for it. Falling asleep is a largely automatic process, and we don't notice most of the things that happen while we're doing it. One that people often notice consists of images flashing through their mind, as our normal vision goes to sleep, and the 'inner image' system takes over.

Remaining Aware While Falling Asleep

Falling to sleep as slowly as possible can be a powerful technique. "The twilight state" is a complicated environment where we can detain any of our senses, ways of thinking, or emotional patterns for questioning, so to speak.

I used this technique every day at a time when I was

doing five hours of spiritual practice a day. I would lie in bed with my palms flat down on the bed, feet completely vertical, while keeping my head absolutely straight, waiting to fall asleep. I'd remain aware of the sound of my breathing – of course. Now, it's impossible for me to fall asleep in this position. I would lie there and weird stuff would happen. My body would seem to move (which can be a harbinger of an out of body experience) and occasionally images would flit through my mind. The main thing I remember is a compelling sense of depth and inner silence.

One night as I fell asleep, I had a strange sensation in my chest; a brief, low-pitched vibration as though a tightly-wound watch spring in the center of my chest had suddenly lost all its tension. The next morning I awoke feeling more "clear" than I had ever felt. For now, the point is this: the Twilight State is *phenomenologically* similar to opening the third eye. We're suppressing the vision from our two eyes in favor of "inner sight", in both third eye states, and in the twilight state. However, we pass through several kinds of dreamless sleep immediately after the Twilight State, and we can't create any memories in dreamless sleep. Most dreams we remember happen in the last hour before we wake up, and Twilight State experiences are easily forgotten. The longer you can stay in that state, the more you'll remember from it.

Unlike the previous exercises, it will be helpful to do our third eye exercise (taking your visual attention away from your eyes) longer than just one or two minutes at a time. It can be combined with most "eyes closed" meditation techniques very easily, so long as you don't have to strain. If you're trying, you're doing it wrong. Stay relaxed.

Opening the third eye may sound like a lofty spiritual practice; something for accomplished Yogis and meditating monks, and those "fated by their karma". It does indeed take extra effort to accomplish it. It has a grandiose reputation, and the exalted words used to talk about it make it seem like we *should* want to pursue it. I don't think anyone should assume that it's worth pursuing as a spiritual discipline on its own. Not everyone is prone to success with it, and there are people who don't find the idea of "second sight" so appealing. Emotions can eclipse our psychic perceptions, and developing the detachment and equanimity that supports psychic perceptions just isn't everyone's cup of tea. Some people are more engaged with feeling love, for example, and don't want to learn how to stand aloof from their own emotions.

If we accept that psychic skills are real, and Charles Darwin was right, then psychic skills are an evolutionary adaptation that contributes (or once contributed) to the survival of primate species. I expect that primate psychic skills evolved mainly to help us relate to others, find food, and avoid dangers.

The best place to use the psychic skills we have *naturally* (as they evolved to help us survive) is in relating to other people. The third eye exercise we just looked at is well worth pursuing, but look for its initial effects; its "first fruits" in intuition, empathy, and emotional connections with other people. Ignore flamboyant claims that it will let you see into the three worlds of existence, see everyone's aura, or diagnose medical problems that doctors can't find. All of these skills might rely on third eye "vision", but they all depend on other skills, too. If you're just beginning your search for spiritual insight, you probably won't know which one of them you're most prone to. The best way is to apply yourself to a spiritual practice (meditation, yoga, chanting, or the exercises in this book) and see what comes up. Each sensation it creates; each shift in your personality as the months of practice go by, can tell you what direction to take *from there*. You can only be on the wrong road if you know where you want to go. It's not possible to take a wrong turn if you're wandering ("not all who wander are lost" – J.R.R. Tolkien).

If you imagine that you are going to become psychic suddenly (which is rare, but not impossible), you have to pursue it until something *clicks*. It might be subtle, but if it isn't clear enough for you to notice it, then it hasn't really happened. As we've seen, psychic imagery appears from the right hippocampus. However, the hippocampus is guided, modulated, and controlled by other brain parts, especially the emotional and social ones. Even if you do become a *seer*, you may not be able to choose what kinds of things you'll see. Don't try to control the process too much. Spiritual growth is often a matter of *allowing* things to happen - without trying to force anything. Micro-managing yourself isn't going to help.

We're a social species. Psychic skills and intuition help us relate to other people. Any such skills would have been heavily rewarded in our early evolutionary (and tribal) history. Mothers who could do it probably had more children grow up to adulthood because they could respond to what was in their children's minds when they were very young, and been better able to meet their needs. Men who could "read" other people would have been seen as natural leaders. The psychic "athletes" in this area would have been shamans. Empathy between lovers would have helped keep families stable, and anyone who could remote view herds of animals would have helped keep the people from starving. Psychics of any sort would have made their tribes fitter and more able to survive, when their perceptions were accurate.

Let me tell you a story. There was an anthropologist in the Kalahari Desert, where the women carried their babies in slings. After a couple days with the tribe, he noticed something. The slings were always clean and the babies were always clean.

He went to one of the women and asked "what do you do when your baby has to shit?"
And she said "We take them out in the bush."
"Wait a minute." (White man pauses to think). "How do you know when your baby has to shit?"
The woman said "Are you stupid? How do you know when *you* have to shit?"

The electrical activity in our brains creates corresponding magnetic fields, and these faint magnetic fields bear information copied from their electrical source. If the baby's brain tells it that it needs to go into the bush, that information, encoded in magnetic fields, is available to its mother, because there is nothing that can prevent the information from reaching her brain[a]. However, if she's distracted or just not sensitive, she might not notice it. I suspect that the difference between that Bushman (!Kung) mother and today's mobile-phone carrying, TV watching, "facebook engaged" mother is that the bushman woman's mind has far less competing information, and she is more able to feel her own body, passing on the sensations coming from her infant.

Everyone broadcasts their brain's electrical activity through the magnetic fields it creates. If you have kids, you know that when they cry one way it means one thing, if they cry another way it means something else. One laugh means they're being tickled, another laugh means they're happy, and another means that they see the humor in a situation. You can pick up a lot from their worldly social cues, but there seems to be also a more subtle level - where there's a direct transmission of information between their brains. The difference between the Kalahari mother's brain and your mother's brain is simply that nothing stood in the way of that information, and the Kalahari mother *adverted* to it.

---

[a] Magnetic fields never stop. They decrease according to the classical law for fields (gravitational or magnetic), falling off with the "inverse square of the distance." There is no way to shield or block a magnetic field. When a person's brain is electrically active (and that's all the time), it produces magnetic fields with the patterns and timings of its electrical activity at work in them.

Remember that this skill (like many others) should be different in humans than in other primates, because we can verbalize the information we get through our psychic perceptions. Language gives us another way of dealing with other people. Being even a little psychic means we have less shit to clean up than otherwise – if we're sensitive enough to know when it's coming.

I had a few moments like this with my own daughter when she was an infant. One of them really stands out for me.

She was perhaps five days old, and my wife and I were sleeping next to each other on a bed. We hadn't gotten a proper crib yet. We took a big overstuffed chair and put it right up against our bed so she couldn't roll out of it, and kept her right next to us. That worked fine. I think it was in her fifth day of life that I woke up in the middle of the night with an awful sensation of prickly heat. It was really unpleasant, and just as soon as had I became aware of it, I saw her face in my mind's eye.

At the ripe old age of five days, her face was already indelibly imprinted in my mind. My impressions were like this: Prickly heat. Baby's face. Listen! *The baby is fussing.* So I reached down to pick her up, and found that there were too many blankets. She was too hot. So I picked her up, opened up her blankets, cooled her off, wrapped her up again, held her for a few minutes till she went back to sleep (they sleep easily when they are five days old), and put her back down and then everything was fine.

I think *active mind's eye* may be the best name for the state called an 'open' third eye. When our visual attention is separated from our eyes, the only images that are available are the ones that come from within, like imaginations and memories. Remember that the right hippocampus is the source of the mind's eye, and it's also the master of seeing (and creating) contexts. When it drops its inhibitions, it can produce images that fit a context. The combination of inner images and the contexts that give them meaning can be enough to make valid psychic perceptions, even if we don't think it's a magical power. Seeing it this way, as a natural skill, makes it more a matter of common sense, and less of a supernatural ability.

If Kalahari babies have the same social sophistication as American babies, then they would probably know that shitting in the wrong place makes people unhappy, just by the tones of voice and facial expressions on the adults around them when they did it. It makes me wonder: was the mother *feeling* the baby's need to shit or was the baby *telling* the mother that it needs to go into the bush? The answer is "I don't know."

I believe it's possible to send information from one person's mind to another, and according to several psychics I've talked with, there's a way to do this.

"Sending" Messages Psychically

There's a technique some psychics say can 'send' simple thoughts to a person telepathically, if you know them well enough to be able to imagine the sound of their voice. Quiet your mind, go into whatever trance you can, and imagine their voice saying something you want them to think or telling them whatever you want them to know. I've put this to the test a number of times and it often seems to work, though it doesn't seem to have any power to force them to *obey* the thought or its intentions, and it appears to have no effect when people are excited, intoxicated or have mental health problems.

Some years ago, a friend of mine and I were having breakfast together. While were talking, I told him "I can impose a word onto your mind" and he said "Great. Go ahead and try." He worked in a spiritual center, with Yoga, meditation, spiritual coaching, and vegan food, and he was open to psychic phenomena. At that time, America has just invaded Afghanistan, so the word was being used a lot. It could come up in a conversation, but it wasn't a common word. Now if I had picked the word 'polynomial' and he wasn't a mathematician, the term could never have come up. If I had chosen the word 'sat-chit-ananda', (Sanskrit for 'truth, consciousness, and bliss') and he didn't know anything about Hinduism, the word would never appear in his mind. I had to pick an uncommon word, but one that could come up in the conversation naturally. Afghanistan was an ideal word because the US had unfortunately just invaded it.

I said "I'm going to write down a word and put the paper in your pocket". This is a little bit of showmanship. It could have gone in my pocket just as easily, but I put it in his. The shaman must be a showman. It's a rule of thumb. Without a touch of showmanship, the shamanism won't be as interesting. A few feathers to gesture with, bowls full of smoking herbs, rattles, drums, sprinkling water and other such things can make it a good show. There weren't many entertainments early in our evolutionary history, but the shaman's ceremonies were one of them. The shaman was a performer. It was (and still is) part of their job and it doesn't diminish their spiritual skills in any way. It keeps them from being boring, so that people want to attend their ceremonies. I've met skeptics who seemed to think that using showmanship means that the shaman is a fake. That's like saying that a psychology professor isn't a real teacher because they use profanity in class.

After writing the word "Afghanistan" and putting it in his pocket, I imagined the sound of his voice saying it. I was actually talking with him, so it was easy to imagine the sound of his voice. After a little while, he started talking about a friend of his who was working in a "new age" store; the kind with textiles from India, Hindu statues, incense, astrology books, and that kind of thing. He said:

"Yeah, the manager doesn't completely get it. He's Afghanistan."
"He's what?"
"He's Afghanistani…"
"You mean, he's *Afghani*?"
"Yeah, that's what I mean."
"Please look at the word in your pocket."

He took it out. Afghanistan. He said "Well, Okay." He was a spiritual practitioner. To some people, this would be miraculous and blow their minds, but to him it was just confirmation of what he already knew. I was preaching to the choir. The point is that I was able to impose the word on his thoughts. It can't be used as an underhanded trick; it sounds possible, but it isn't. A person's long-standing mental habits will always supersede passing brain noise, and even if the same words were spoken out loud, not everyone will be equally sensitive.

If I had used a phrase instead of a word, and the phrase was "I must shoot myself now." It never would have worked. All of his instincts for self-preservation would have rejected the thought right as it came up. That's why it's difficult to use any kind of psychic or esoteric skills to get people to do things they don't want to. You can't get them to harm themselves, for example, unless they're prone to such behavior, and even then, the instinct for self-preservation will be an obstacle. You can't use it to seduce people for the same reason – unless they're already thinking about saying yes.

Hearing the sound of their voice in your head may create a kind of resonance with the brains' electrical activity and the magnetic fields that go with it, and they would have heard it hundreds of thousands of times, each time used their voice.

"Calling" people psychically

There is another classical technique and it seems to dovetail with the right hippocampal involvement in psychic and intuitive skills as well as its role in inner imaging[73]. I have heard of it in two contexts. One was in Carlos Castaneda's books, including *The Teachings of Don Juan*, and the other was a temple in north-east Thailand. It was a monastery in a village where my wife (at that time) was from, and her family took me to visit there a few times. I tried my best to learn their ways, including their religion, and they came to trust me. I had a good job at the time, and I donated money to the temples whenever I went there. There were two temples in the village. One was the main temple which had some money and had the occasional rich visitor coming from Bangkok, and the other was a crude barn of a temple where everything was old and worn and nothing was worth any money. Their Buddha statue was carved from wood. The other one had a large brass statue. There was a rich temple and a poor temple, and I liked the poor temple.

After one visit, I found myself remembering this temple too often. The though kept running through my mind: *I have to go to that temple; I have to go to that temple.* I remembered the technique from the Carlos Castaneda books. I went to see the abbot, who sat with one other senior monk. I said "Look, there is a technique where silence your mind, and then visualize a person's face in your mind's eye. If the person is far from you, they will think of you, and if they are near, they will come". They had been using this technique on me and I called them on it. I knew it. I said "You guys are messing with me." And the two monks started laughing.

I mean literally. These were staid, dour; sour looking,

slightly malnourished Buddhist monks, rolling over one another with laughter. They kept telling me: *boo-aht, boo-aht*, which means 'ordain' or 'shave your head and become a monk'. They were trying to get me to pine for the peace and tranquility of the monastic life. If they were gentler about it, I might not have felt that my thoughts about their bucolic temple were out of place for me.

I'm not going to shave my head but I really enjoyed the connection with them. These were meditation monks. They didn't do many rituals or ceremonies. They didn't live to collect donations. Everyone who came there did meditation, sometimes for several hours a day, and they practiced a little white magic from time to time.

The technique appears to make use of the brain's capacity for inducing a kind of sympathetic resonance between the activities in a pair of brains. It's probably the basis for all empathetic and telepathic abilities.

Let me summarize our techniques for working with the hippocampus.

1) Imagining space is behind you on one side but not the other.

2) Imagining illusory feelings of movement to work towards having an out of body experience.

3) Separating your eyes from the direction of your vision.

4) Imagining people's voices in your mind, saying things

that you want to communicate to them.

5) Imaging their faces in your mind's eye as a way to call the person to contact you.

Remember that you can only use these methods for good, because any attempt to use it for harm will initiate people's self-defense and self-preservation instincts. You can't hurt people using numbers 4 and 5 above, so don't waste your time trying, and don't train your mind to waste your energy that way.

Todd Murphy

Chapter Three

Some Body-Centered Techniques

The Caudate Nucleus.

The Caudate Nucleus

Now we move on to the caudate nucleus, or just "The Caudate". *Caudate* means 'tail'. It got that name because it looks like a tail on the end of another structure. The caudate nucleus has been called the *emotive visceral integrator* which just means it integrates your emotional state with your body's state of relaxation or tension. When you get angry and tense, that's the left caudate nucleus connecting your emotional response your body's state. If you feel waves of relaxation going through your body while meditating, that's the right caudate nucleus at work.

The amygdala and hippocampus have distinct *themes* in their functions. The amygdala's themes are emotion and relating to others. The hippocampus' themes are space, spatial perception and reasoning, information processing, memory and inner imaging. The caudate nucleus has a very broad range of functions, but its principle theme seems to be *bonding*[74]; motivating behavior that helps us connect with others. Interestingly, it even helps more when we're speaking a second language than our native language[75].

One of its themes is in the way it helps guide us towards rewarding behaviors, which calls for some learning skills, some "reward circuitry", and some emotional functions. In humans, The Caudate also plays a major role in the experience of love.

It also contributes to *prosody*[76], the "felt" aspect of language. Prosody refers to tones of voice, how loudly or quietly we speak, and the phrases we emphasize. It also helps is with our choice of words[77]. When we know that a word is too strong to use, the caudate nucleus alerts us, and tells us to quickly find a gentler one. The caudate nucleus helps us choose to say 'Excuse me, but that's my coffee you've picked up' instead of 'Fuck you, that's mine'.

The limbic system has its checks and balances. On the right side it supports relaxation; that's where meditation and psychic skills are. On the left side, it "does" arousal; that's where excitement, anger, lust, and happiness are to be found. When we feel excited after something good happens; that's the caudate nucleus. If you give good news to small children, they can literally jump around in their excitement and chant things like "We're going to the movies. Going to the movies. Going to the movies." That looks like behavior from the left caudate nucleus activation, turned into behavior.

There's a phrase we use in neuroscience, *behavioral correlate*. It refers to the behavior that acts out a moment of activity in a part of the brain. We can think of behavior in terms of activity in the specific brain areas that support them. When we speak of a *behavioral correlate*, we imply that we're not only concerned with quantified data ("the numbers") about these brain structures; we also pay attention to what people actually do, think, feel and experience when they're busy. We objectify the brain, not the person, when we study behavioral correlates. We won't use the phrase much in this book, because there are ordinary English phrases that do just as well (like "acting out"), but the idea that running in fear, for example, is a *behavioral correlate* of right amygdala (the 'seat' of fear) excitement helps to understand how brain parts drive the states of consciousness that motivate our actions.

On the left, the Caudate participates in love, like romantic love[78], erotic love, and maternal love[79]. For example, the caudate nucleus is more excited when a woman with a newborn baby is talking to it[80].

One that I still puzzle over is a report that that the caudate nucleus on the left side is instrumental in unconditional love[81]. This experiment was talking about feeling love for strangers; in this case, people with "intellectual disabilities", so they might have actually been examining feelings of compassion, but then, compassion may not be so different from unconditional love.

One other technique that seems to initiate caudate nuclear response is rhythmic dancing[82]. It's also been called *Trance Dancing*; dance that repeats the same movement over and over again. It's one of the world's oldest spiritual practices.

Archaeologists have found camp sites dating back tens of thousands of years with intact fire pits. Their excavations found that the fireplace just kept going deeper and deeper, showing that the people returned to the same camp site as they followed the herds each year. As they danced around the fire, they packed the earth in a circle around it. And in many places, the hard-packed dance circles are still there for archeologists to find. [83]

Circle dancing.

Dancing in a circle is an ancient spiritual practice. If you watch modern trance dancers from tribal societies in videos on YouTube, or the National Geographic channel, or go to a Native American *pow wow*, you'll see that each person has their dance, and they repeat the same movements again and again. Ritual dance is different, as I understand the phrase. In ritual dancing, everyone repeats the same movements. In *spirit dancing* (as I've heard it called), there is no right or wrong way to dance. People take it for granted that dance is a way of getting in touch with the spirit world, getting closer to your tribe, exploring their own minds, feeding their dreams or whatever they choose to call it. I'm willing to assume that there was no such thing as religious orthodoxy for our early ancestors, so all movements were fine. The emphasis is always on finding *your* dance. If the way your body naturally moves is silly, then you do a silly dance. If the way you move your body naturally is elegant, then you have an elegant dance. But whatever it is, it's yours, and you can go into an altered state by repeating its movements over and over again.

And I think this also applies to normal chanting (not to be confused with recitations, which we discussed before). The chants are called mantras, like *Om Namah Shivaya, Hail Mary*, or *Namo Kuan Shih Yin Pu' Sah*[a].

Repeating things over and over is a standard shamanic technique. Chanting, dancing, whatever it is, if it's repeated often enough, it will eventually send you into another state of consciousness. In one case history, the Caudate Nucleus responded to chanting practices more than other deep brain parts, though some surface areas responded more[84].

There are a couple of spontaneous sensations that look like the subjective experience of an excited caudate nucleus[b]. One of them is tingly sensations (pins and

---

[a] This is a Chinese mantra, meaning "I invoke Quan Yin, the Bodhisattva of Compassion"

[b] This is based on the similarity between the caudate nucleus's themes and emotional body sensations ("chills") in response to sex, music and even horror movies. In fact, there is very little evidence about which parts of the limbic system are involved with these sensations (called *parasthesias*).

needles and chills that run through your body). The brain's "reward system" is activated when we have chills while listening to music[85]. The Caudate Nucleus is an important part of the reward system, though its direct links to chills from music hasn't been studied yet.

Most of the time, if music makes you want to dance, it won't give you chills, and if it gives you chills, it won't make you want to dance. We have to pay attention to music *consciously* to get chills from it[86], while dancing is much more about "letting go" and sharing our attention between the music and our bodies. Dancing is a *social* behavior[87], while being engrossed in listening to music is much more solitary. The emotional impact of music is much stronger when we listen to it with our eyes closed[88], letting us pay closer attention to it.

There are passages in Beethoven's 4th and 5th piano concertos that will sometimes send chills running up my spine. Beethoven was the master of the orchestral slow movement. He could slow his compositions down almost to stillness and then, in that tempo, compose for the spaces between the notes. There is a single note at the end of the 2nd movement of his 4th piano concerto that sends chills through my entire body, but only if I'm really paying attention.

Tingly sensations happen in other context. Lots of people have chills, pins and needles; (the technical name is *parasthesias*), and a lot of people have them during sex, which is right on the border between relaxation and excitement. Good sex is both relaxed and excited. These words may be mutually contradictory, but few readers here will have no such experience and everyone else will understand what I'm talking about. Yes, there is such a thing as relaxed excitement.

Our next exercise appears to have its basis in the caudate nucleus, and we can approach it more intelligently now that we know something about what the *caudate* does.

The Divided Body Exercise.

It's important to sit up *straight* for this one. Make the midline of your body vertical. Put your hands on your knees. Don't cross your hands or your feet.

As before (sorry if this bit gets repetitive), I'll ask you to take a moment, breathe a little deeply, and put yourself into whatever trance you can.

Mentally draw a line down the midpoint of your body, running from the top of your head through the tip of your nose, the middle of your chin, sternum, navel, all the way through your torso. Just imagine your body is divided into its left and right sides. Next, pay attention to what you feel within the right side of your body. Ignore the left completely. In fact, ignoring the opposite side may be more important than focusing on the right.

Next, focus on the left side of your body, and ignore the right side. Be aware of the quality, the texture, the tone; the firmness or softness within each side of your body. There isn't any exact word for the sensation I'm asking you to notice, so I have to use metaphors. Did you notice any difference in the "timbre", the texture or quality of the left and right sides of your body?

Like all our other exercises here, some people have clear responses, some have vague ones, and a few have none at all. It's very rare for anyone to have strong responses to *all* of them, because that would imply that all three of these structures (Amygdala, Hippocampus, and Caudate Nucleus), are more sensitive than normal, and then we would start moving from the realm of spirituality and into the realm of psychiatric disorders, unless the person has taught themselves (or been taught) to live a disciplined spiritual life. If your limbic system is overly sensitive, you're likely to experience some kind of trouble at some point during your spiritual growth – if that is, you work hard at it.

Most people find that one side of their body is light, clean, empty, and warm. The other side is darker, more solid and a bit heavier. One side is more relaxed, and the other more tense.

Like most of our exercises, it's okay to do it for a minute or two. You do the exercise, feel the effect, and then move on. You can stay with it longer, but don't cling to the feeling it creates. If the feeling slips away, open your eyes, and come back to it later. Doing it more often is better than doing it for longer periods. Doing it 20 times for one minute is better than once for twenty minutes. The only one that's good for *sustained* effort is the one in the last chapter where we separate our visual attention from our eyes.

Most people can change their dominant eye just by

focusing their attention on the non-dominant eye's visual field, making one side of their vision fill their awareness as they neglect the other side, though I've never heard of anyone who made it shift *permanently*. You can do the same thing with the two sides of your body, allowing the side that feels good to dominate your sense of your body.

You may find that its just as easy (or difficult) to stay aware of one side of your body this way as it is to keep your eyes 'set' to the non-dominant one. Like all mental exercises, it gets easier with practice. It's not easy to "re-train" the Caudate Nucleus. It has higher thresholds than the amygdala and the hippocampus (it's less sensitive and harder to control), so you don't be disappointed if you can't keep the more pleasant side of your body "in focus" for long in the beginning.

However, for many people, doing it briefly can mean instant relaxation. When something stressful happens, take a breath into the side of the body that feels best for you, so to speak. Breathing "into" an area of your body just means imagining that your breath is something like a hydraulic system, and you are pushing it into some part of your body. We're trying to take a "nuts and bolts" approach, so we'll avoid the exalted language some "new age" writers use.

Its effects are clearer than our other exercises, and more people seem to respond to it. The caudate nucleus is more similar from person to person than the amygdala or the hippocampus. It doesn't matter very much who *you* are or how likely you are to resist new states of consciousness it might bring up, when you try to get it to respond. When I say *resistance*, I mean it in a very neutral way. Resisting the right amygdala with its fearful functions is a good thing. Resisting the left hippocampus with its tendency to become excited[89] and think about things too much (it plays a role in schizophrenia[90]) helps us feel good.

Compassion and Love

The caudate nucleus on the left side supports the experience of love, so it's natural to wonder if there is a way to activate the caudate nucleus to create it. There is such a technique, though this one is not only based on neuroscience. It also uses a classical Buddhist method.

To evoke the sensation of love deliberately, you can practice a technique from a book called *The Path of Purification*, (The "Visuddhimagga"), a 5th century Buddhist text. It's sort of an early Buddhist grimoire; (a book of magic), though it's about working with your mind, not spells or incantations.

The author (Buddhaghosha Acharaya) said an easy way to develop "compassionate loving-kindness" (*Metta Karuna*), was to find someone or something that you love. It was written for Buddhist monks, and they aren't supposed to love women, and, having renounced the world, they were away from their families, another focus for love. They gave up all objects of love when they ordained as monks and renounced the world. Under the original Buddhist rule, monks and women could not have even the most trivial physical contact. To this day, some traditions even dictate that monks should not allow women to hand them anything directly. They have to put them on a special tray used for that purpose.

Buddhaghosha said that whenever you see a baby, the pinnacle of cuteness and adorability; give it your full attention. Look at it and allow the feeling of love, and your response to their cuteness to appear with full force. *Don't* renounce "compassionate loving kindness". Monks and nuns renounce many things but that feeling isn't one of them. Eventually, you stop paying attention to the baby, but you stay with the feeling. You won't hold it for very long at first. The next time you see a baby, do it again. Sustain the feeling as long as you can, knowing it won't last. Buddhists are dedicated to remembering that things don't last ("all is impermanent").

See the baby. Find the feeling. Hold on to it after the baby has gone. Eventually you reach the point where you can carry the feeling what he called *compassionate loving kindness* for longer and longer periods.

Perhaps a better phrase for our modern world might be *love and a response to cuteness*. Cuteness creates unique responses. It's a beautiful feeling. I think that's why videos of little kittens are so popular on the Internet. They inspire love and kindness.

They're cute. They have their big kitten eyes. They're vulnerable, and we want to protect them. We want to feed and cuddle them.

Find the feeling of compassion as often as you can, whenever the opportunity presents itself. Eventually you see a person who isn't young and cute and adorable and cuddly. Nevertheless, you maintain that feeling while you relate to *that* person. You're working towards seeing everyone with the same "eye". It's been called the *eye of compassion.*

It's a way of looking, a feeling that invites a distinct gaze. An angry gaze is one thing. Compassionate, gentle, loving, cute, adorable, cuddly, delicate, tender *fluffy baby bunny rabbit* feelings call for a different gaze; the eye of compassion. Start applying it to everyone. You can develop it whenever you have an opportunity to love someone, but without any attachment or desire; without wanting anything from them.

Just because you think a baby is cute and adorable doesn't mean you want to take it home, just like the way we don't want to capture a baby baboon just because it's cute. This kind of compassion lets you be involved, even as you keep your sense of detachment. It's easy to love other people's children without being attached. People who say "I love kids – other people's kids, but I don't want to have one" aren't fools, nor are they being cynical about parenting. Rather, they're enjoying the sensation of love without attachment or any need to possess or control anyone. You can't control babies anyway.

You can begin by focusing on the side of the body that's most relaxed. The combination of a gaze filled with love, an actual lovable object, a relaxed body and a touch of dispassion make a powerful combination when if you practice it with diligence. It's a lot easier than it might sound, too. All you really "do" is focus on the side of your body that feels good, look at something or someone that inspires loving feelings, and let the rest happen on its own.

Remember that we're a social species. We evolved in the context of ancient tribal cultures, where everyone was at risk if the tribe didn't work together. There were tremendous rewards for loving other people.

Angry outbursts are usually frowned upon in tribal cultures. It happens from time to time, and when it does, they're full throated in their anger. They're just as expressive as anyone else. However, tribal peoples know that it's one of the worst ways to resolve conflicts, and someone who does it too often will never command respect from their people[a].

We are evolved for love, but not unconditional cosmic spiritual love. We're evolved to love one person at a time. Our natural state (living according to the circumstances in which we evolved) is to anticipate the needs of those we love. We are adapted to go out in the

---

[a] My understanding of tribal cultures comes from my studies in anthropology, my Native American teachers, the time I spent in a rural village in northeast Thailand, studies in shamanistic spirituality and even a course in archeology. After all of that, I know that there are no exact criteria for tribal customs and laws. Even more importantly, I learned that tribal ways are mostly a matter of common sense, based on the principle that the needs of the group outweigh those of the individual.

forest, find a piece of perfectly ripe fruit, remember that a certain woman really likes it, take it back to the village, give it to them and hear them say "Awwww." Survival (and success) of the *socially* fittest favors those who can get others to smile and look at them thankfully. We evolved to seek out the gratitude of others as one of our primary social rewards. The reason is simple. People who inspire admiration achieve higher social ranks than those who don't[a].

Gratitude is one of the few emotions that doesn't have an agenda. It doesn't get you money or sex or power or anything like that. Feeling grateful is one of the very few emotions that cannot be perverted or tasked to serve greed or a hidden agenda.

There is one other emotion that is equally "clean"; the sense of being awestruck at beauty. Yes, I can be filled with admiration at a woman's beauty and I can also feel a more undirected awe at what I see in nature. Skies, landscapes, sunsets; you name it. There is no agenda there, and there never could be. You can't seduce a moonrise or borrow its money.

We are evolved for compassion, love, friendship, response to cuteness, gratitude and a wide range of feelings and behavior that help us bond with other people.

---

[a] The more socially fit a person is, the higher their social rank will be, and males in the upper ranks have more mating opportunities. Females in the upper ranks receive more help in raising and feeding their children.

I believe that the tribal ways we lived and related to each other in our earliest history are the ways we're best adapted to. The healthiest and most natural way of life means living within those behavioral, psychological, and spiritual pathways; according to our first (tribal) agendas and priorities. Which means that I, who spend so much time in front of a computer, may be living one of the most unhealthy ways imaginable. So are children being raised by parents with cell phone addictions.

Spiritual Healing

There were a lot of things we didn't know when we first appeared as a species. The generations that followed learned quickly, but we knew very little at first.

The first generations of humans didn't know which plants will heal you and which ones will make you sick. It took generations for a full pharmacopeia of herbal medicines to be developed. I have met American Indians who claimed they could pick a root, bite on it, suck on the juice, and they will know instantly what it can be used for. They might have a psychic response to what the plant brings into their body. They could also be sensitive to the chemical processes as they start to digest the juice. Their brain responds with a feeling or sensation, and they fill in the details. This is a non-verbal kind of cognition, so we would expect the right hippocampus would play a strong role. Such shamans can take the sensations that come up when they gnaw a root and understand immediately which diseases offer a context for it, the way some animals,[91] including primates[92], eat plants outside their normal diet to heal themselves. If gorillas can do it, then people probably can, too, no matter what skeptics who are opposed to alternative medicines have to say. However, until the first humans developed their herbal medicines, there was little they could do when they were sick.

So what did we have for healthcare and medicine in our very earliest evolutionary history? You only have to look at today's tribal peoples to see that they used shamanic healing practices. Witch doctors, Medicine men and spirit healers are only three of their many names.

Spiritual healing is different in different cultures. There were no rule books or guides to medical procedures, and there were different practices in different nations. When someone was sick, the shaman might walk into the middle of the village, hold a sacred object over their head (or not, depending on the culture), and sing a ritual song. The words of the song might mean something like this:

> *'Someone is sick. Everyone who wants to heal them, come. Come now. Come on. We are all going to heal him. Let's all pray together that they get better.'*

I've made this up, of course. It's a summary of several such traditional tribal announcements I've either heard or read. In one I personally saw (an engagement ceremony)[a], the village elder of a Thai village entered

---

[a] In the Nahnglong (A.K.A. "Nang Rong") district of Buriram province, Thailand.

the room, yelling at the top of his voice for the Spirits to come. Everyone within earshot knew what it meant, and what kind of ceremony they were doing (Animist, not Buddhist). It was a simple message, of course, but to the point. The Shaman, like the chief, could act as a "town crier". Anyone can in most tribal cultures, but not everyone will get any attention.

Sometimes the whole tribe would come. Sometimes just a few would participate. Then they would gather around and sing as the shaman prayed. The patient would be surrounded by a group of people, all focusing their attention on them and their illness. It could not help but re-affirm the person's value to their group, which tends to enhance immune system function[93].

In spite of being focused on an individual, it's still a social event for the others, just like an infant blessing (such as a baby's baptism), or a womanhood ceremony. The sick person goes into a mild altered state, brought on by the ceremony, which could facilitate brain-to-brain connections between them and the other participants. Remember that this appears to be a right hippocampal function, and that the same brain part is also involved in music and rhythm. Songs and drumming are usually important parts of shamanic healing ceremonies, and we can't rule out that the music and drums facilitate brain-to-brain interactions, because both music[94] and telepathy[95] are associated with activity in the hippocampus.

The limbic part of the brain that appears to support positive social behavior is the amygdala on the left, supported by its neighbor, the left caudate nucleus.

Activation of the left hemisphere is immuno-enhancing[96], and in spite of the many positive cognitive functions in and around the right hippocampus, the right side is known to be immuno-suppressing[97]. There is evidence that people with positive (left-hemispheric) emotional "styles" activate their immune system more readily that those who default to negative emotions[98]. Depriving the left hemisphere of blood is more likely to create immune system problems than the same kind of brain damage on the right.[99]. For a few individuals, too much meditation, a right-sided task, can bring their health down[100]. People are energized when they are angry, and anger has been seen to enhance immune system response[101], while less angry people are likely to heal more slowly[102]. Many of the brain's functions look cross-matched, with negative emotions on one side and pessimistic thinking (*cognitions*) on the other.

Andrew Weil tells a story[103] about a man who was dying of an illness, and had an episode of rage over his death so intense that he eventually dropped from exhaustion. When he woke up, he found that his sickness had gone. The extreme excitement in the left side of his brain (supported by the opposite side, of course) seems to have spilled over into his immune system pathways, making them hyperactive for a time. Weil didn't tell us how things turned out for that patient in the long run, but even a short-term improvement in immune function will be a blessing to the patient. Anger is mostly a left-hemispheric function[104] [105], and it can ramp up the immune system enough to do some good. Of course any therapies based on it might be dangerous in other ways.

A group of people gathered around a sick person to do a shamanic healing is a collective, social event, but there is evidence that suggests there may be more to it than that.

As we saw before, brain to brain communication relies on the magnetic fields that exist throughout our brains, which can account for telepathic information sharing. There is ample evidence that EEG patterns can synchronize between pairs of brains, in studies quite unrelated to psychic phenomenon. Japanese researchers have found synchronization between EEG signatures during human speech[106]. This phenomenon has been independently validated[107] by French researchers, who see communication with other brains as a potential property of all the connections in a brain[108], or even the entire nervous system (a "connectome"). Italian neuroscientists have come to the same conclusion, saying that it correlated with "global" (whole brain) efficiency[109]. Researchers at the Mayo Clinic have called this kind of connectivity between brains a "prelude to telepathy[110]." And other researchers have demonstrated brain-to-brain communication by forcing two brains to cooperate in playing a computer game[111]. Still others have used encoded streams of words to tease out brain-to-brain effects[112].

One researcher concluded that showing that two brains can share information would tend to support the validity of spiritual healing,[113] and Dr. M.A. Persinger's experiments with magnetic stimulation[114] have shown that two brains can indeed do just that.

Everyone sings together in a shamanic tribal healing. Rattles and drums make their sounds. The smoke curls upward. The ritual acts are performed, and everyone believes they're working to help the sick person get better[115]. All of this has an effect[116] [117], even when the ritual is in an operating room instead of a tribe's sacred space[118]. It starts with the recognition that positive attention from other people is a healing factor, especially when you know they want to heal you. Certainly, science understands that loneliness [119] and a lack of community is bad for immune system function[120], and that some medical treatments work better when people have religious faith[121], which would include shamanic beliefs.

Group prayer. [122]

There is also another technique. It's often called *healing by laying on hands*, and I'll explain how to do it or rather, how to *learn* to do it. Some readers will make rapid progress, others slow. We can think of it as a form of prayer, sometimes with the community calling out to the spirit of the sick person, but more often praying to God or a spirit to intercede for them.

There have been many studies and experiments on the "healing power of prayer". Several of them used "placebo controlled, double-blind" protocols. The people they were praying for were randomized and the ones praying for them were assigned a participant number. They were told to prayer for an anonymous sick person, like "patient number 23", and the researchers found that nothing happened[123]. In other studies, people sat together the way that born again Christians do in their spiritual coaching; in fellowship with one another (as they call it). I've also participated in this kind of group prayer. They lean down and sit with their hands folded in prayer, praying out loud ...

Lord Jesus, Jesus help my brother. He can't stop drinking. Lord Jesus, put your spirit into him Lord. Heal him and make him whole. In the name of Jesus, in the name of Jesus, in the name of Jesus.

Unlike the anonymous, sterile, laboratory protocol-controlled prayer[124], this kind actually seems to work[125]. It appears to help people recover from illness[126] and surgery more quickly[127]. It helps overcome behavioral and substance addictions. It looks like not much happens unless there is a personal connection, if the prayer isn't done in person or about *actual* people, and not individuals who correspond to data points. When people pray for people they've seen in photographs, but never met in person, it's more effective than randomized, placebo controlled (and anonymous) double-blind studies.

Applying placebo controlled double bind conditions to prayer studies means that you have to expect people to avoid praying for the control group. *Lord, don't help those people in subject pool "C". Let them die so we can prove that prayer is good and Thou art real.* Who (besides people in hate groups) is going to ask God _not_ to heal somebody? It's more likely that they will pray for all of them ("Those sick people"), and ignore the instructions from clinical researchers, who seem to lack both compassion and any kind of prayer life.

Anyone with a mature prayer practice will find this ridiculous. Standard scientific method appears to fail in these cases. People and their prayers are not pills, and the placebo controlled, double blind method was designed to test medications, not human behavior. When a chemical medication is under study, only one thing is being tested; a chemical. Many factors are at work when someone prays. There is the depth of someone's absorption in prayer, their relationship to the person they're praying for, the words they use in their prayers, their emotional sensitivity, and their capacity to establish brain-to-brain communication, to name only five. Few prayer studies take any notice of these elements. They treat all prayers as being the same, just as pharmaceutical studies assume that the medication, and the doctors who administer it, are the same for all subjects[128]. A chemical may be the same for all subjects in an experiment, but there is huge variation between prayer styles, the beliefs that support them, and their intensity.

Prayer should be studied in *social* contexts because that's how a lot of prayer is actually done, and it's how we evolved, with community prayer as a feature of tribal life. There's no such thing as a placebo prayer, and no one prays without having some idea who they're praying for. The context is so unnatural that its rigorous experimental conditions can eclipse the very phenomenon it's trying to study.

Todd Murphy

Chapter Four

Spiritual Healing

Introducing Karmu, a spiritual healer.

Karmu (Edgar Warner) 1910 – 1989. A Boston Area healer.

I used to have a teacher called Karmu. He was a spiritual healer. There's even a film about him called *Karmu: A Place in the Sun*. His main work was spiritual healing, especially "by laying on hands". Karmu didn't have a group to gather around him and sing songs, shake rattles, play drums and fan smoke around, replacing the tribal community's role in healing the sick. He had to rely on himself, and his main tool; his hands, and the *energy* he could produce with them. Naturally, the word *energy*, as used here, is very different from the way scientists use it[a].

---

[a] In physics, *energy* refers to the capacity of a body or a system to do *work*. Work is done when the point or region of application of *force* is changed. A force is anything that alters or tends to alter a body or system's state of rest or uniform motion in a straight line. This state is called *inertia*. Some skeptics consider that any other use of the

159

There is some evidence[129] that what healers and spiritual teachers call *energy* is actually a *force*, like the "*force* of gravity", or centrifugal *force*.

"Healing power" may be a magnetic phenomenon. One Japanese study on "Chi" healing found that a few of its subjects had "extraordinary" magnetic field strengths around their hands; without the matching electrical current scientists would expect[130]. Another study found similar effects, coming from both the hands and the head[131].

Healing by *laying on hands* always appealed to me more than any other psychic arts, and I've managed to practice from time to time in the years since Karmu died. He taught me the art, but I was never one of his superstar students. That's fine with me. Being a faith healer was never one of my goals, though I admire the skill very much. We may be impressed by the CIA remote viewer, but someone who can stop our pains when the doctors can't deserves our honest gratitude.

Karmu didn't have a tribe, but he had skills that we don't always find in tribal healers. His social skills were

---

word *energy* means that the person using it is mired in pseudoscience.

Even though I'm a scientist, I have no problem with the same word having more than one meaning. This skeptical attitude would be like a doctor ridiculing any use of the word *depressed* except referring to diagnosed depressive disorders. In fact, the word *depression* has entered common English usage to refer to any kind of sadness. Medicine has no monopoly on the use of its vocabulary, and science has no sovereignty over the word *energy*. Indeed, there is no authority empowered to grant it.

extraordinary. He could perceive people's moods and their states directly. He only needed one look at a person to instantly know about their health and psychological history, and, most importantly, their inner milieu at the time they came to see him – in that present moment. This may have compensated for the lack of a village he could call in to pray with him, as shamans would have done in the early days of our species.

People were often desperate by the time they came to see him. They usually arrived only after getting nowhere with mainstream medicine. Most of the time, he wasn't the first person they went to. By the time they came to see Karmu, they were usually scared. They would walk into his room, which had no door. He had no doors, except the front door. Everything else was completely open, as he himself was.

When they arrived, he would start his work. He once told me "the shaman must be a showman", and his show was mind-stopping. People would literally drop their jaws as he showed them his unique evangelism for the first time. His "rap" (which was never exactly the same thing for any two people) went something like this:

> "You've come at last! I was waiting for you! You are one of the high and holy ones, one of the Medicine Beings, and I'm going to help you. Whatever you need, I give in gladness. I'm going to give you everything I have, and then we'll triple it with what comes down from the heavens. I can see your halo. Someone get me some sun glasses! My third eye opened when you came in

the room and I can see what's going to happen. You shall be healed and made whole. Your soul will be ravished by a divine force. Then, amidst the songs of a million angels, you will make the blind see, the deaf hear, and the crippled throw away their crutches and walk, shouting *hallelujah*! You shall rise, and you shall shine. You'll be high-sprung and far flung. You will be a god given child. Just sit down here and I'll work on you. I'll invoke the invisible powers, and the great god Oogoo-Moogoo. I'll help you like I helped that blind rabbi who went right out and rotated his tires during a blizzard. You're a VDC with a DPE. That's a *very decent citizen* with a *definite plus element*. You will be my spiritual child. You're going to have sixteen beautiful blondes in bikinis massaging your toenails. You'll be known to the nations as the Holy one; the Most High. The world will know your name. The earth will know your footsteps."[a]

Another published rap[132] from Karmu says this:

You know, you fellas are very very fine, I like what I see...you're a couple of high grade citizens. Look at this one. Isn't he beautiful? Look at those teeth! What's your name sir? You don't belong with us ordinary people, you belong with the gods. You're really two beautiful cats. I

---

[a] This is a paraphrased rendition. No two of his students would ever do it the same.

got 50 women looking for fellas like you. … I'd like you to leave your name, address and phone number. How many toes you got on each foot?

He could keep this up as long as he wanted, without ever repeating himself. He was a carnival barker at one point. I think that he also once worked as an auctioneer. His past was always a bit obscure, and you never knew when he was recounting facts, storytelling, or giving an impromptu inspirational sermon. He had a close friend who was a professional storyteller, called "Brother Blue"[a], and they influenced one another deeply. They both had a peerless "gift of gab". His talk therapy was part of his shamanistic ritual. Such ceremonies have been validated in a few medical case histories.[133]

After a while, no matter how sick they were, no matter how scared they were, they would eventually start to smile. He'd make them feel appreciated, ebullient, and jubilant, and only *then* would he put his hands on them.

Healing Hands – The Technique

The technique is simple. It starts out by simply being aware of the palms of your hands. As before, you need to close your eyes and put yourself into a light trance. Hold out your hands, or put them on your lap, with the palms facing upward.

---

[a] *Brother Blue*, The late Dr. Hugh Morgan Hill, was a street storyteller in Boston, who later became a professor at Harvard University. Several good videos of his art can be seen on YouTube. When a filmmaker went to interview Brother Blue, and asked him to tell a story about Karmu, Brother Blue, who was never at a loss for words, said that he couldn't do it. It was too heavy (profound).

Next, imagine that there are holes in the palms of your hands, and that you're breathing through them. When you exhale, something; some diaphanous liquid, smoky, rarified invisible substance comes out. Imagine it goes in when you inhale, and out when you exhale. Just sit there for a few minutes and allow that sensation, as it ebbs and flows in time with your breath.

Some people feel pulsations (not like blood pulsing), or a mild sense of pressure. I've heard a couple of people say it was as though their hands had magnetic fields that were repelling something. You might feel tingly sensations, or feel that your hands are warm. A sensation of heat is the best one for spiritual healing work, but it may not appear until after you've spend some time practicing.

This exercise seems to work for more people than the others in this book, and more easily. Most people can get a sensation from their palms simply by imagining it. Why? Because 200,000 years ago, when our species first appeared, it was how everyone was healed. Anyone who couldn't learn it would have less to offer their tribe. It seems to come easily to nearly everybody with any spiritual inclination, and that's about two out of three people[a]. It doesn't only have to be introduced in the womb or learned as you grow up. It can also be something that we can pick up from other people,

---

[a] This is based on normative data (profiles of the normal population for comparison with data from unique populations) and the neural profiles of people who report frequent altered-states experiences, uncommon spiritual beliefs, and psychic perceptions.

through brain-to-brain communication. The more it's done around you, the more you'll be able to do it. Its survival value would have been so high that any method of passing it on would also have a real evolutionary value. Today, it's a rare kind of gathering, and few people today learn such skills through such telepathic means, but it could have been a common event at the dawn of our species. Many tribal cultures don't do it deliberately, or just let it happen naturally, just by touching the sick person, as they connect with their feelings.

Now, let's do the same exercise again, but this time with one difference. As with all our exercises, it begins with a light trance with your eyes closed. Again, put your hands in front of you with the palms facing up. This time, forget about your hands at first. Find the most intense emotion you can, except fear[a]. Think of anything that made you happy. Here, we're looking for a positive emotion. It makes no difference where it comes from. Even remembering something that gives you an excessive sense of self-importance (an "ego trip") is just fine. A feeling of joy usually works best (better, for example, than a comic mood), but you can use almost any good one. Grief, poignancy, or nostalgia will also

---

[a] Fear isn't germane for healing work. Healing includes getting rid of the person's fear, and it will be harder if the healer is also in fear because, both positive emotions and immune enhancements are associated with left-hemispheric processes, while fear involves right hemispheric activity. Beyond that, there is the possibility that brain-to-brain communication can add a touch of fear to the process, which would make it less effective.

work, but only if they're strong enough. In general, the stronger the emotion, the more it will help the process. You should do a little experimenting on your own to find the feeling that's easiest for you to achieve on demand.

You may wonder why our emotions should play such a strong role in this kind of healing work. I think it's because, we were motivated to heal people by the love we had for one another when we first appeared as a species, 200,000 years ago[a]. We were also *less* motivated to heal people we *didn't* love. Like those from competing tribes, or the overly-aggressive ones among our own people. If someone had a personality that alienated the people around them, they would be less likely to find help when they were ill. The Shaman, of course, would probably still pray for them, but "difficult people" would have less chance than those who inspire affection. Over time, their lower recovery rate after shamanistic healings would impose a gentle evolutionary pressure in favor of nice people, at the expense of the ones most folks just didn't like. It sounds like the opposite of compassion, but when people are free to choose who they associate with; they're more likely to choose people who don't bother them.

---

[a] This number keeps changing. In 1997 or thereabouts, I recall reading that humans were 40,000 years old. Now, we're five times older than that. In spite of my enduring interest in evolution and anthropology, I've seen the number change so many times that I will probably regard it as a "soft" number for the rest of my life. I've never advanced any hypothesis that would be valid if we were one age, but invalid if it were different. Anthropology keeps changing the playing field, but it never stood me up on a first date, or borrowed any money from me. Overall, it's been kind.

Evolution prunes out more people who don't help their group than those who do. Because living in together in a human society is our strategy for survival, anyone that alienates people invites their own exclusion. Evolution is more compassionate towards our social groups than it is to individuals, although evolution doesn't actually feel anything. It's an automatic biological mechanism, with less mercy than any human bureaucrat. Just as the bureaucrat is only concerned with their paperwork, and not the person they relate to, evolution is merciless when the needs of individuals are in conflict with the needs of the group.

When someone was sick, the crier, the shaman called out to the people 'So-and-so is sick let's all come together. Let everyone who wants to heal him gather together.' If that was your good friend, or someone you loved; if it was your brother or sister, or someone who grew up at your fire place, you'd probably say "Oh god, they're sick. I have to help." Your compassion for the person that you're trying to heal both drives and sets the limit of your healing abilities. If you don't feel any compassion, heartache, or nostalgia for the days before they were sick, no grief for what might happen if they don't get better, then your 'healing power' is probably going to be a little weak, in their case.

Such group healings are "paid for" by the pain or sadness that other people feel because of the illness. Every smile in a person that gets better is traded for a tear from the ones who heal them, and if they don't feel anything, then they're probably not healers, or the person who needs the healing doesn't inspire them to join in. This mostly applies to the ordinary people in the tribe. We should expect it'll be different for the shamans, who usually have an obligation to help. You have a choice. You can follow the Shaman's route, and begin with joyful moods.

Shamans spend a lot more time practicing and honing their spiritual skills than most people would. For the shamans, the range of emotions that can facilitate healing should be much wider than for others. Besides this, healing work can also be done in other states of consciousness. Going on "spirit journeys" (a.k.a. "astral travel") into other "spaces" (which relies on the hippocampus, the brain's engine for spatial perception, inner imaging and "contextualization"), then they can retrieve information about how to help the sick person.

There seem to be three kinds of spiritual healing. The first is community prayer; the second is "laying on hands" and the third is "spirit journeying", also called *astral travel*.

Astral Travel

Let's look at *spirit journeys*. I'm going to allow myself a little room to speculate to help us see how a shaman, who journeys into the sky or the underworld[134], might use the experience to help heal a person. After seeing a hundred fevers and tasting several hundred herbs, plants, tree barks and lichens, the shaman would have a feel for their characteristics, and their hunches would be more reliable than other people's. To undertake a "spirit journey", a shaman would have to disinhibit ("open up") some hippocampal functions. The hippocampus is the source for inner imagery of all kinds, most importantly the content of our dreams. This includes visions and astral travel, which I think are a lot like 'waking lucid dreams'.

The world's spiritual traditions tell us tales of inner landscapes[a], alternate 'realms' of reality, other dimensions, the dreamtime, the Astral Plane, and the kingdoms of heaven and hell. I think these "spirit realms" are actually different names for very similar experiences. Heaven and hell, with their blissful and painful aspects, are reserved for those who have left the 'physical plane'. According to several religions (and accounts of visions of heaven and hell), they both involve *powerful* emotions. They're both infinitely large and both will exist for eternity. Each has a master (God or the devil). Finally, both are known through the stories of mystics who've seen them in their visions. In fact, the only difference may be that hell is filled with fear, and heaven is a place of bliss. Hell is filled with fearful scenes, and heaven with beautiful ones.

I believe the same neural mechanisms that put us into the *alternate reality* of our dreams are also the foundation for *other realities* of visions and shamanic journeying. The first generations of humans, like all tribal peoples,

---

[a] Scientific Reality Check - Here, *Inner landscapes* refers to endogenously generated episodic hallucinatory environments, including all images found therein. Spirit journeying refers to gaining and maintaining access to the concomitant state(s) of consciousness.

valued their shamans, and encouraged them to develop their skills. The older shamans taught the younger ones, and over the generations, their body of knowledge would only grow, unless the lineage was broken when a shaman died without leaving any students, which can explain why tribal cultures don't all use the same healing methods.

These tribal sorcerer's apprentices were taught that they could learn secrets, encounter profound teachings and receive amazing insights while they're in the spirit world. They would then be predisposed to *expect* to learn things in visions, but just as importantly, to ignore more mundane perceptions.

The hippocampus will be more active in this state than in normal consciousness; it's excited and busy trying to extract new information from what it already knows. This sensitive, responsive, and 'labile" state can disinhibit ("open") the hippocampus' capacity to put things in context, and allow new insights.

During a spirit journey, the shaman might see a few herbs or roots, and intuitively "know" that these are the ones their patient needs. He knows that they are the right herbs the same way we know that anger is red, or that chocolate sauce shouldn't have curry powder in it, and why affection is warm, while being ignored is cold. The same sense also tells us that love is soft, and anger is hard. I believe shamans first learned which herbs to use for which illnesses through this kind of *qualitative association*, and that they searched for the esthetic qualities in herbs that were the most "opposite" to the qualities of the illness. They search through the herbs they find in the spirit world, or wait for a spirit being to provide the right prescription. In fact, they may be searching their memories, but in a unique and non-linear way. Some shamans would be able to call up a lucid dream and find what they need there.

The spirit journey opens (disinhibits) their thought processes so they can let go of thinking in words, and see associations and contexts they could only see in this altered state. The same process will let them "explore" psychology, how their prey might behave, the way people relate to each other, as well as what will happen when people act out their emotional patterns in different contexts. The line between intuitive understanding and psychic perception is blurry, but our ancient tribal ancestors probably didn't care about that. Besides this kind of altered-state, subjective, qualitative thinking, there is also brain-to-brain communication, allowing shamans to perceive illnesses telepathically, giving them intimations of what it feels like to be the patient.

This uncommon phenomenon is called *mirror-touch synesthesia*. Usually, it's not a skill at all, and is best known as part of phantom limb phenomenon[135], where a person loses an arm or leg and then finds that they still have sensations from the missing limb. If they see a video of an arm being touched with a pointer, they feel it in their missing arm.

It's been linked to empathy[136]. The phenomenon doesn't happen with films of dummies or mannequins; it only appears when actual *people* are in the film. It may be that shamans who have such a skill have learned to disinhibit ("open") it so that it's available when they need to try to heal someone. But, this is speculation. There are cases of people acquiring synesthesia [137] (where the senses are mapped onto each other, so that colors have sounds, shapes have tastes, and so forth), and there are also cases of doctors[138] using mirror-touch synesthesia to help them find diagnoses. There is a published report of a massage therapist using it to feel their client's response to her work[139]. One researcher has offered the hypothesis that "highly empathic individuals could be predisposed to strengthening existing pathways between observed touch and felt touch"[140]. If someone were not "highly empathetic", they probably won't be a shaman in the first place, but there is no way of knowing if this skill was more common in our early history, or if shamanic training ever included learning it.

Admiring shamanic skills doesn't mean that we don't respect doctors. They often stay up at night, racking their brains, doing research, searching for the best treatment for you, and checking other case histories. Such doctors are engaged with their patients, but they're still *physicians* and that's not always the same thing as healers. We respect them, but we don't admire them the way we love the priest that truly comforts us, prays with us, and shares our tribulations "in fellowship," or the shaman who "goes to spirit" to find a cure for our ills.

I recognize that tribal religions are the product of our evolutionary heritage and cultural history, and that they take a seemingly infinite number of forms, though they all serve the same functions. I also recognize that my more modern way of seeing spirituality isn't going to be better for people living with older religious ideas. So, when I meet a Muslim, I don't say anything to display my own different views. It's much more pleasant to show off my understanding of *their* views, if I feel like showing off at all.

I greet them with *As-salamu alaykum* (Peace be unto you), and I use phrases like *Al ham du lillah* (Thanks be to God), and *Inshallah* (If God is willing). Muslims seem to love hearing them, even though they know that I'm not a *believer*. It shows respect to their religion and with so much hostility towards Islam in the USA (at this time of writing), it's a bit refreshing for them to hear such phrases from people of other religions[a]. Just using one of these phrases says "I respect your religion", and they like hearing that. I do the same thing with Christians. I never *say* that I'm a member of their religion; I just talk with them using the vocabulary of their faith. This attitude has let me learn from many people with deep spiritual lives, even though I disagreed with their beliefs. Many of them look like shamans to me, working in the context of modern religions.

I used to know an old evangelical Christian woman

---

[a] Take note that there are some Muslims who feel that these phrases should not be used by others, but so far, I've never actually encountered one. I've heard that some feel its okay for *Peoples of the Book* (Jews and Christians) to use them, but not others.

("Gwen"). She was 84 years old when I knew her. She told me that she sometimes spent six hours a day in prayer. I had never said anything to show that I didn't believe the same things she did, though I did tell her so. Once I was talking to her and I told her that I was worried about a problem, and she just said "Let's pray together."

She took my hands. *"Lord Jesus. Move your power on this man. Give him the help he needs. Send him what he needs to overcome this difficult time."* She went on like this for a while and finished her prayer, saying *"In the name of Jesus, In the name of Jesus, In the name of Jesus,"* and then she stopped and heaved a sigh, and I felt something run through my body. Of course, I also prayed for her, and the health of the people around her, using a restrained version of Karmu's prayer style.

I got on my bicycle to go home and found I was almost too happy to steer it. Her hands, grasping mine, had uplifted my mood. The (so-called) *energy* had come through both of our hands. Later on, I asked her 'Do you feel heat in the palms of your hands sometimes?' and she said "Yes". She also told me that she used it to do the *Lord's healing work*.

> "Heal the sick, cleanse the lepers, raise the dead, cast out devils: freely ye have received, freely give." (Matthew 10:8)

She told me how she had once healed a person of muscular dystrophy, and added "That tired me out. Whenever I did that, Satan attacked me. The Devil didn't want that one to be healed, but I *wasn't* going to let him torture that child." She agreed with Karmu's teaching that heat in the palms of the hands is the best sign that a healing was really happening. She also said that she wasn't the one who did the healing. It was actually God, she said, working through her. Many, if not most spiritual healers say that they aren't the ones who heal people. They feel that a "higher power" is working through them, and they themselves aren't the one doing it.

This brings us to an important variation on our "Healing hands" technique; combining it with the "sensed presence" imagination. The words used here to describe it aren't long enough to give it the importance it deserves, so I'll just ask you, dear reader, to take note that this is an *important* addition to the technique.

Letting The Higher Powers Do The Work

To do it, you need to "breath energy" into your hands, and at the same time, imagine a presence behind you and on your left[a].

If you're like most people, you'll find that either evoking the sensation of a presence or the feeling of heat in your hands is easier for you. One or the other. If you can call up a sense of a presence easily, then establish that sensation before you focus on your hands. If your hands respond more quickly, or noticeably, then begin by focusing there. A few people may not be able to do both

---

[a] Unless you are one of those uncommon people who find that a presence (behind you) on your right feels better.

at once, but they may still find that they can switch back and forth between them. Once you have both techniques working at the same time, simply make the *presence* the object of your prayers or intentions while you're healing someone. There are few "wrong" ways to pray, so don't be concerned with that aspect of the process. There may be none at all, but however you do it, make sure that the words don't fill your thoughts completely. Let the words stay in the back of your mind, and stay focused on both sensations; in your hands and in the feeling of a presence.

Once you have a knack for this practice, you can add still another variation: Keeping the presence <u>above</u> you, as well as behind you, on the left. This can raise the emotional impact of the presence, making your healing work more effective.

Prayer is the most common and natural support for healing practices. Our species seems to be configured so that we're a lot more able to pray than to meditate. Prayer probably makes up 80% of the spiritual practice done in this world. It's a reflection of both our evolutionary heritage, and our brain's architecture. The amygdala, the deep-brain basis for prayer, is more responsive. It changes its activity more easily than the hippocampus, the limbic basis for meditation.

Although you can rehearse on your own, these healing exercises can really only be used in actual *healing by laying on hands* sessions. To inject a healing tone into other things you do in your daily life, take a page from

Karmu, who had no qualms about calling himself[a] "*the Wonder healer, the Holy Man, the Black Christ of Boston*".

Here's a quote from Dale Carnegie[141]:

> Be "*hearty in your approbation and lavish in your praise*".

Remember that you're a human being. You are *homo sapiens*, and the original context in which your kind existed was tribal. There was very little room for anger or hatred. Arguments happened, but the tribe's cohesion depended on resolving them without force, and avoiding anger and hatred as much as possible. I won't tell you to love everybody the way Jesus said, because those words have been repeated for 2,000 years and look at what's happened. Christians usually don't love each other; not the way Jesus said to. His words alone are not enough. But then, Christ set the bar so high that we cannot help but grasp something higher if we try to fulfill his command[b] to love everyone. "Reach for the stars and you might touch the clouds".

Truth.

Truth is synonymous with God in most religious

---

[a] Karmu used this flamboyant language to set a mood, and enjoyed its absurdity.

[b] John 13:34: "A new command I give you: Love one another. As I have loved you, so you must love one another. By this everyone will know that you are my disciples, if you love one another."

traditions. In Islam, one of the names of Allah is *Al-Haqq* ("The Truth"). Jesus said "I am the way, the truth, and the life …" (John 4:16). The Buddha said the four insights into the end of suffering were its "noble truths". Their funeral mantra is *Ram Nam Satya Hai*; "The Name of God is Truth". Hindus say that the self is grounded in two triads. The first is truth, consciousness and bliss (Satchitananda). The second is truth godliness, and beauty (Satyam Shivam Sundaram). In Judaism, "The seal of God is truth[142]".

The truth is a spiritual point of reference, but I think it instructs us to avoid lies more than to stay truthful about everything, all the time. We need untruth just as much. We need folk tales. We need the Tooth Fairy. We need myths, jokes, and nonsense. We need people who can spin a good yarn. Karmu understood this, and he knew the difference between a liar and a bullshit *artist*.

"A deception that elevates is dearer than a host of low truths." – (attributed to Alexander Pushkin)

If you want to be a healer, gentle reader, my advice is to pay compliments whenever you can. There are many cultures where this is normal behavior, so never mind if your compliments are 'true' or not. Remind people that others around them appreciate them – that they have a good social "rank", as the anthropologists call it. Healing - making people feel good – through our words is a simple and easy way to step into the cycle of healing other people.

Karmu's lessons to me (and my rendering of his shower

of compliments and encouragement) might show you that the truth has nothing to do with it. Words that make people feel good are more helpful than the "true" ones.

Go ahead and tell people that one day they'll fly. They shall rise above - even if they are on their death bed. Tell them that children will sing their names. Tell them that they're one of the anointed ones; sons and daughters of this earth. I've told at least a dozen women, some of them over 80 years old, that they were the most beautiful woman in the world, _and_ the Queen of Persia ("Long live Your Majesty"). None of them seemed to mind, and all of them smiled.

> "Men turned to stone when they ceased to believe in the beauty of the impossible" (Arabian nights).

When someone would point out that Karmu's encouraging words weren't always true, he would give them a mischievous smile and say: "So I lie a little?"

Say good things to people in whatever way is fun for you, because if you aren't having fun, your words will lack power, and if you are having fun, you'll _feel_ that what you're saying is worthwhile, and that makes it easier for the person you're talking to feel they're true. Never mind the literal truth.

The _feeling_ is what's healing.

Todd Murphy

Afterword

How do you know when it's time for you to step on to a spiritual path? The answer is simple. You feel the urge. Even when you know it's time, it can be daunting to find a path that works for you. There are so many teachings, disciplines, and kinds of meditation, and they come from a wealth of different spiritual traditions. Each one will tell you that their way is the best.

I've been working in the area where religion, spirituality and mysticism meet science for over 20 years. Along the way, I've met hundreds of spiritual seekers and practitioners. Some of them were very deeply involved in their inner work, and one of their most common questions is why we need such a field. Why bother? Why not just feel the magic of living on this vast and beautiful earth, mindful of our impermanence, and loving everything we can? Why try to explain it?

My answer is that, like our ancient cultures, our tribal

languages, our folklore, and the earth itself, our older religions are under threat from the all-pervading modernization of our world. Science has called almost every religious belief into question.

One of the rules of science is that simpler explanations are more likely to be true than complicated ones. But when a human behavior or emotion looks simple, then we're probably not seeing it clearly. Judging traditional spiritual beliefs according to the standards set by laboratory work or scientific journals doesn't work. They were all put in place long before the scientific method was invented, and their claim to truth was based on faith and personal experience. Lab experiments (and the ideas they set out to prove) are designed to stand up under the rigorous conditions science demands. Traditional religious truths are designed to stand up in people's minds, one person at a time. The value of prayer lies in how it makes us feel, not objective measures or proof of its effects. The same is true for the truths found through meditation, yoga, or any of the other older spiritual practices.

The world is giving up many of its older religious beliefs, like creation in seven days, the Buddha's journey to heaven to give his teaching to the gods, divine laws subjugating women to their husbands, the death penalty for witchcraft, or the transubstantiation of bread into the body of Jesus. The trouble is that when just one of a religion's beliefs is cast aside, they *all* become questionable. If one decides that there is no God; no single creator of the universe, then prayer seems to have no value. Science has made it harder to believe in God, and so fewer people pray, thinking that prayer is pointless if there is no God to hear their prayers. It's not, and, strangely, belief in God isn't a prerequisite for doing it. Prayer and rituals are for the benefit of the people doing them, and belief in God is just one of its natural contexts[a]. The atheist's conviction that prayer is useless because there is no God is a mirror image of the religious belief that we should only pray to him. It implies that skeptical atheists think that they know what's hypocritical in religious belief and what isn't. It would be like giving racists the right to judge what is or isn't fair play in Afro-American politics.

A truly rational view would see that prayer is a human behavior, and we should try to understand it without regard to the beliefs it traditionally rested on. We eat when we're hungry, and we don't need to know how the specific nutrients are helping us. In the same way, we pray or meditate to act out our spiritual feelings, without knowing how it feeds our minds and brains. Rejecting prayer because we can't believe in God can leave us unable to act out our spiritual sentiments. Just as some people need to take vitamins, but others don't, not everyone feels the need for a prayer life, but many people do, and feel they that something is missing without it.

---

[a] Some religions, like Buddhism, don't believe in a creator. Others, like the Lakota "Way of the Pipe", where the creator is a mystery ("The Great Mystery"), have a God, but few teachings about him. Hinduism has a creator, but no one prays to him (because another God, Shiva, put a curse on him).

This book has a short preface and not an introduction because it will be an Amazon title, and Amazon has a feature called "Look Inside" that lets people look at the first few pages of a book. Introductions to books are often less interesting, so this book has an 'afterword' at the end instead, so that people "previewing" the book can get a better idea of what it's is actually about. It's a neuroscientist's guide to new kinds of prayer and meditation, uncovered while studying the brain's role in religious and mystic experiences.

Spirituality needs science to find explanations for the effects of spiritual practices and the value of religious beliefs, so that the people who do them and humanity can both continue to benefit from them. Religious *practices* should be preserved, even as medieval religious beliefs are fading from our cultures. We're letting go of the dogma, but still working on its replacement.

When science has good reasons why people should do spiritual practices (work on their "being"), we'll soon find them being taught in science classrooms, where students are expected to do the learning but will, of course, be free to practice as they choose – away from school.

Mystic practices, like meditation and yoga, can be taught in schools, if the emphasis is on the science supporting them, and not the religious beliefs they grew from.

One of the hallmarks of a valid scientific idea is that it can be tested in a lab, through library research, or by mathematical analysis. In contrast, the test of a mystic practice is how it makes us feel, both while practicing and in our daily lives. These two different ways of finding the truth mean that the truth of science can mean very little to someone who's trying to achieve spiritual growth. The insights from individual people doing inner work have little or no value for scientists, who dismiss them as "anecdotal" and thus, invalid evidence.

Another reason why science should study spirituality is that new sciences create new technologies. Knowing what the brain does in spiritual moments makes it easier to find new ways to attain them. If science understands spirituality, we can look for new "inner technologies"; new portals to the spirit, and use them to enrich our spiritual lives. This book shows some ways to put some of this science (in the growing field of *neurotheology*[a].) into practice.

We've gone through a series of spiritual exercises that use simple imaginations to help create real experiences and sensations you can use to enrich your spiritual life. It also explains how you can use these imaginative and emotional exercises to help you find the spiritual practices that are most likely to work for you. Most of these exercises are based on brain science and work by asking you to imagine something on both your left and right sides, one at a time. You'll notice a difference in how good they feel on each side. Without a classical

---

[a] "The scientific study of the neural correlates of religious or spiritual beliefs, experiences and practices. "

dogma to guide us, we should hold on to the science behind them, or they'll seem like they have no foundation at all. Our spiritual exercises appear to activate specific brain parts, and we spent some time talking about what they do. The ones that gave you a stronger response point out directions that your spiritual life can take; without asking you to spend months doing meditation, or pray for years before you can see if the way of prayer is good for you.

The sensed presence exercise points to the way of prayer.

The open space and 'third eye' exercises point to the way of meditation.

The 'divided body' and the 'healing hands' exercises point to the way of service to others.

The better each of these worked for you, the more you can trust the way it points to.

Imagination is more powerful than most people realize, and we use its power to excite the brain parts that support spiritual feelings and sensations. These are deep in the brain, in the *limbic system*. They support so-called "primal" feelings, thoughts, and sensations. What comes out of them is always routed upwards, to the brain's surface, so that they're the raw material for our "higher" brain functions. We can express fear using words, by calling for help. We edit our expressions of sexual desire using our social skills, to avoid offending or boring our potential partners. Anger is filtered through our social skills, so we can express it responsibly. The limbic system rarely works on its own, letting our sense of responsibility, from the "higher brain" direct how we act out the needs and desires it imposes on us. Our higher brain is motivated by the need to be in harmony with the people we live with, relying on the religious beliefs we learn throughout our lives. Religion is an explicit expression of frontal lobe functions, nonsense and wisdom, both. Private spirituality, including mysticism, is the repository of the limbic functions we use to be happy with our own behavior, beliefs and connections to other people.

Some of our methods are modern inventions, and some are traditional techniques that show a clear basis in the brain or in the anthropology of tribal life; the first way of living in human history, and the one we're biologically adapted to. That means 'the one our brains evolved to live in.'

This isn't a book on the psychology of religion, or using spirituality to 'recover' from anything. I take the view that the past, including early childhood experiences, like abuse or illness, may create a need for spirituality, but looking at our early years of life doesn't offer much guidance once we grow up. An anguished childhood may create the background, but looking at it won't help us grow spiritually once it's over. The best way to begin a spiritual journey is by looking at what we feel and what we can do, as we are *now*. The maps may have been put there by issues in the past, but you have to read them in the present. The simple exercises in this book can tell you what kind of sacred practices will be best as you are now.

It makes no difference whether your discontent at living in this material world (or in your own mind) comes from a hard childhood, a broken relationship, or a philosophical crisis. What's important is finding your way to something better (or maybe just less boring) than a commonplace, mundane life. "Inner work" can make your life better or more interesting, but you can't find your way forward by looking at the past, and you can't find your path by looking towards a future you can't predict or control. Looking to the past to try to figure out what to do now is like telling a car mechanic about the accident that broke your engine, but they need to know what's wrong with the car *now*. Sometimes, it's useful to know what caused a car collision, but usually the auto mechanics do their job best by opening the hood, and looking at the motor.

It seems like every mystic tradition tells the world the same thing: That anyone can feel God's presence; everyone can succeed with mindfulness meditation. Anyone can be psychic. Anyone can gain serenity with Yoga. Anyone can attain peace. Anyone can achieve bliss. Anyone can be a success.

Each person is different, and so is each brain. This means that these things aren't equally easy for everyone. Some people make rapid progress moving down a spiritual path, while others struggle, often for years, to get any results. One of the problems with the ancient traditions is that they're usually based on the revelations or visions of just one person. Jesus felt that God was with him so intimately that he said "I and the Father are one". The Buddha found his bliss by disrupting the self so radically that it could never be the same again[a], and he was a bit disparaging about using prayer[b] to achieve happiness. In contrast Jesus taught prayer, not meditation. They each felt that their way was best for all, and the spiritual traditions that followed them often still speak as though their ways were the only ones.

Joseph Smith's visions are the sole source of Mormonism. The Prophet Mohammed (blessings be upon him) is the sole source for Islam. Jesus, and him alone, is the ultimate source for all of Christianity.

Today, we find spiritual teachers who say that slow progress is a sign that you are "working through your karma" or that your faith isn't strong enough. A few even appoint themselves as psychotherapists, and will

---

[a] After his final enlightenment, he said, comparing the *ego* to a "house builder, I hurried through the round of many births: Painful is birth ever and again. O house builder, you have been seen; You shall not build the house again. Your rafters have been broken up, Your ridgepole is demolished too.
My mind has now attained the unformed Nirvana and reached the end of every sort of craving". *Dhammapada*, 153-4

[b] If … (long life, happiness, beauty, status, and rebirth in heaven) … were to be obtained by reason of prayers or wishes, who here would lack them? It's not fitting for the disciple of the noble ones who desires long life to pray for it or to delight in doing so. Instead, the disciple of the noble ones who desires long life should follow the path of practice leading to long life. In so doing, he will attain long life, either human or divine. *Anguttara Nikaya*, 5.43

tell you that you have to resolve issues with your early childhood or past lives to move ahead. I believe that most of the time, this is just foolishness being offered by teachers who can't tell which spiritual practices are best suited to each person. A Buddhist teacher lacking "skillful means" might say that this isn't true for *them*, and will suggest that a person try a *different* meditation when their first one doesn't work out. Their "radar" often won't detect people with an aptitude for contemplative prayer, for example. Priests, ministers and pastors can't see when a person who has trouble going deeply into prayer might better off doing yoga, chanting, or visualization techniques.

My work is in the field where science and spirituality meet; and how the brain creates or participates in spiritual experiences. It's convinced me that no spiritual practices work for everyone. Each person is unique. Meditation will always be a dead end for some people, and there are others who will never enter any but the shallowest states of prayer. However, a person who can't get absorbed in either one might still be able to abandon themselves to verbal chanting.

There are also people who never have any spiritual or altered-state moments of any kind, and such people may be less likely to be good candidates for prayer, mediation, chanting or any other kind of spiritual work, but they're also less likely to be interested in this book.

Healing

One perennial spiritual technique is *spiritual healing*,

especially *healing by laying on hands*. I believe that this was once humanity's most important, perhaps our only, way of responding to illness and injuries. When we first emerged as a species, about 200,000 years ago, we didn't have a pharmacopeia of medicinal plants and herbs. Not at first. It took time to learn which plants to use, and how to prepare them. While this was happening, we had to rely on shamanic healing methods. Some of them are very easy to learn, when we ignore the doctrines about them, and instead focus on their raw sensations and techniques.

Some of the exercises here are my own inventions, but they also take from older spiritual traditions, as well as some direct instruction from Karmu, who gave no formal religious explanations and avoided the kind of sensationalism and outlandish claims we see in televangelist healers[a]. Although they are mostly very new techniques, more than two thousand people have tried them while doing online questionnaires. I've also led groups doing these exercises. Many responded with their feedback, so now we know what they do, and we can be reasonably sure how they work.

We also looked at some scientific research, and took the

---

[a] "And as ye go, preach, saying, 'The kingdom of heaven is at hand'. Heal the sick, cleanse the lepers, raise the dead, cast out devils: freely ye have received, (and so) freely give." (Matthew 10:7-8) Here, Jesus implies that raising the dead is just as easy as healing illness. He set the bar very high here. Even Evangelical Christians, who believe "every word" in the Bible, don't talk much about the apostolic injunction to raise the dead.

opportunity to go over some interesting discoveries in neuroscience. I hope that seeing how your brain is involved in your spirituality, and how ordinary brain parts support extraordinary experiences; will help you in your spiritual life. Extraordinary moments can come with ordinary inner work, if you persist with them, and if yours works for you.

One day, someone might discover some kind of non-physical, unobservable, seemingly unknowable beings that give us spiritual guidance, but for the time being, we're staying within a narrow limit. We'll do our thinking as though our spirituality comes from our minds and brains at work. To do this, we have to avoid explanations based on "subtle energies", magical powers or The Quantum Baby Jesus. Sometimes people respond to that by saying "but that's so limiting," and my response for that, (it's almost a "canned answer") is: "If you want to write haiku, you are limited to fourteen syllables. If you want to do charcoal drawing, you are limited to black and the background color. If you want to be a career parent, you're usually limited to having one child at a time." There are intrinsic limitations in life, and if we accept them the way we accept the rules for haiku, then we can make them work for us. We're working where science and spirituality meet, and they don't speak the same language. All paths have limitations. To stay *on* the path, we're limited *to* the path. Most cars aren't designed to drive off the road, so we limit ourselves to the strip of pavement just ahead of us, and we only turn when we cross another road. That keeps us safe, and keeps the car intact. Yes, it's limiting, but we're so accustomed to staying on the road that we don't mind.

A note on the references:

This book represents a meeting of science and spirituality. To remain faithful to the science, I've given a number of references which appear at the end. Most readers won't need to look up the studies and experiments they refer to, but leaving them out would abandon the very science we rely on. A bit of scholarship is essential when a work is based on science. Just as scientific papers need to cite the works that led up to them, we should acknowledge the huge body of work that laid the foundation for what we do here. There are footnotes on some pages, to provide some background. Some of them are written in more technical language, helping us close the gaps between the terms used in science and the vocabulary of spirituality, religion, and mysticism.

Todd Murphy

ABOUT THE AUTHOR

Professor Todd Murphy is a long-time member of Laurentian university Behavior Neurosciences research group, under the direction of Dr. Michael A Persinger. He is the author of "Sacred Pathways; The Brain's Role in Religious and Mystic Experiences", with Forewords by The 14th Dalai Lama, and Dr. M.A. Persinger (available on Amazon.com) He's published in the Journal for Near-Death Studies, Psychology Reports, *Activitas Nervosa Superior*, and the journal, *Neuroquantology*. His 9-hour lecture series can be seen on www.youtube.com. He is also the developer of the Shakti and Shiva Neural stimulation systems, which made Dr. Persinger's pioneering neural stimulation work, known for their spiritual effects, available to the general public. His studies in *neurotheology* (a term he doesn't really like) began in 1985, becoming increasingly formal until his work found publication in academic journals, beginning in 1998.

A Final Note:

If you're like most people who read this book, you got it online at Amazon.com. If you like what you've read, please take a moment to leave a positive review. Books with more reviews are seen by more people on Amazon. It's the best way to help an author (or a book) get a little more attention. It also helps them to feel good about their work. Leaving good reviews is good for your karma, too. It only takes a moment.

Just log in to Amazon.com, go to the page for this book, and scroll to the bottom of the page, and click on "Write a Customer Review".

Amazon may delete one-sentence reviews as well as off-topic reviews.

Thanks in advance for your kind help.

Todd Murphy

References:

Poerio, Giulia L., et al. "Love is the triumph of the imagination: Daydreams about significant others are associated with increased happiness, love and connection." *Consciousness and cognition* 33 (2015): 135-144.

[1] **Irwin W, Anderle MJ, Abercrombie HC**, Schaefer SM, Kalin NH, Davidson RJ. "Amygdalar interhemispheric functional connectivity differs between the non-depressed and depressed human brain." *Neuroimage*. 2004 Feb;21(2):674-86.

[2] Public domain image from Wiki Commons.

[3] **Miller LA, Collins RL, Kent TA**. "Language and the modulation of impulsive aggression." *Journal of Neuropsychiatry and Clinical Neuroscience* 2008 Summer;20(3):261-73.

[4] **Aurélie Richard-Mornasa**,Et.al. "Emergence of hyper empathy after right amygdalohippocampectomy" *Neurocase: The Neural Basis of Cognition* Volume 20, Issue 6, 2014 pages 666-670

[5] **Schirmer** A, Escoffier N, Zysset S, Koester D, Striano T, Friederici AD. "When vocal processing gets emotional: on the role of social orientation in relevance detection by the human amygdala." *Neuroimage*. 2008 Apr 15;40(3):1402-10.

[6] **Conty** L, Dezecache G, Hugueville L, Grèzes J. "Early binding of gaze, gesture, and emotion: neural time course and correlates." *Journal of Neuroscience*. 2012 Mar 28;32(13):4531-9.

[7] **Persinger** MA, "Neuropsychological principia brevita: an application to traumatic (acquired) brain injury." *Psychological Reports*. 1995 Dec;77(3 Pt 1):707-24.

[8] **LaBarbera** R, Hetzel J "Christian Educators' Use of Prayer to Cope with Stress." *Journal of Religion and Health*. 2015 Sep 3.

[9] **Hölzel** BK, Carmody J, Evans KC, Hoge EA, Dusek JA, Morgan L, Pitman RK, Lazar SW. "Stress reduction correlates with structural changes in the amygdala." *Social, Cognitive and Affective Neuroscience*. 2010 Mar;5(1):11-7

[10] Vaillant, George E. "Psychiatry, religion, positive emotions and spirituality." *Asian journal of psychiatry* 6.6 (2013): 590-594.

[11] **Leitman**, David I., et al. "" It's not what you say, but how you say it": a reciprocal temporo-frontal network for affective prosody." *Frontiers in human neuroscience* 4 (2010): 19.

[12] **Fecteau**, Shirley, et al. "Amygdala responses to nonlinguistic emotional vocalizations." *Neuroimage* 36.2 (2007): 480-487.

[13] **Barwood**, Martin J., et al. "Improvement of 10-km time-trial cycling with motivational self-talk compared with neutral self-talk." *International journal of sports physiology and performance* 10.2 (2015): 166-171.

[14] Public Domain image from Wiki Commons.

[15] http://abcnews.go.com/GMA/International/pope-john-paul-whipped-belt/story?id=9674114

[16] Public domain image from Wiki Commons, provided by www.kremlin.ru

[17] **Horga** G, (Et Al.) "Brain metabolism during hallucination-like auditory stimulation in schizophrenia." *PLoS One.* 2014 Jan 8;9(1):e84987.

[18] e *Chandogya Upanishad* 6.8.7,

[19] **St-Pierre** LS, Persinger MA. "Experimental facilitation of the sensed presence is predicted by the specific patterns of the applied magnetic fields, not by suggestibility: re-analyses of 19 experiments." The International journal of neuroscience. 2006 Sep;116(9):1079-96.

[20] **Bird** CM, Capponi C, King JA, Doeller CF, Burgess N. "Establishing the boundaries: the hippocampal contribution to imagining scenes." *The Journal of Neuroscience* 2010 Sep 1;30(35):11688-95

[21] **Wamsley**, Erin J., et al. "Dreaming of a learning task is associated with enhanced sleep-dependent memory consolidation." *Current Biology* 20.9 (2010): 850-855.

[22] **Brodziak**, Andrzej. "A current model of neural circuitry active in forming mental images." *Medical science monitor: international medical journal of experimental and clinical research* 19 (2013): 1146.

[23] **Jung**, Rex E., Ranee A. Flores, and Dan Hunter. "A New Measure of Imagination Ability: Anatomical Brain Imaging Correlates." *Frontiers in Psychology* 7 (2016).

[24] **Schomaker**, J., and M. Meeter. "Short-and long-lasting consequences of novelty, deviance and surprise on brain and cognition." *Neuroscience & Biobehavioral Reviews* 55 (2015): 268-279.

[25] **Dasse**, Michelle N., Gary R. Elkins, and Charles A. Weaver III. "Hypnotizability, not suggestion, influences false memory

development."*International Journal of Clinical and Experimental Hypnosis* 63.1 (2015): 110-128.

[26] **Loftus**, Elizabeth & Ketcham, Katherine (Author) "The Myth of Repressed Memory: False Memories and Allegations of Sexual Abuse" St. Martin's Griffin, publishers, 1996

[27] **Luders,** Eileen, et al. "Global and regional alterations of hippocampal anatomy in long-term meditation practitioners." *Human brain mapping* 34.12 (2013): 3369-3375.

[28] **Luders**, Eileen, et al. "The underlying anatomical correlates of long-term meditation: larger hippocampal and frontal volumes of gray matter."*Neuroimage* 45.3 (2009): 672-678.

[29] **Nielson**, Dylan M., et al. "Human hippocampus represents space and time during retrieval of real-world memories." *Proceedings of the National Academy of Sciences* 112.35 (2015): 11078-11083.

[30] **Wiener**, Martin, Kelly Michaelis, and James C. Thompson. "Functional correlates of likelihood and prior representations in a virtual distance task."*Human Brain Mapping* (2016).

[31] **Maguire** EA, Woollett K, Spiers HJ. "London taxi drivers and bus drivers: a structural MRI and neuropsychological analysis." *Hippocampus*. 2006;16(12):1091-101.

[32] **Bremner**, J. Douglas; Randal, Penny; Vermetten, Eric; Staib, Lawrence; et.al. "Magnetic Resonance imaging-based measurement of hippocampal volume in post traumatic stress disorder related to childhood physical and sexual abuse: A preliminary Report." ***Biological Psychiatry***, 1997, Jan, v41 (n1) : 23-32

[33] English translation by Abdullah Yusuf Ali.

[34] Andhakara Sutta: Darkness, SN 56.46. Please do not contact me to ask if I think this means that the Buddha knew about Black Holes. I think it's an account of a subjective experience, and not a case of the Buddha remote viewing a collapsed star.

[35] See *Memory*, by Elizabeth **Loftus**, Addison-Wesley; First Printing edition (November 1980)

[36]   The right hippocampus is smaller after stressful ("challenging") events ("post-challenge cortisol levels were inversely associated with total and right hippocampus volumes"). Tessner, Kevin D., et al. "The relation of cortisol levels with hippocampus volumes under baseline and challenge conditions." *Brain research* 1179 (2007): 70-78.

[37] **Harrison**, Paul J. "The hippocampus in schizophrenia: a review of the neuropathological evidence and its pathophysiological implications."*Psychopharmacology* 174.1 (2004): 151-162.

[38] **Persinger**, Michael A., Pauline M. Richards, and Stanley A. Koren. "Differential ratings of pleasantness following right and left hemispheric application of low energy magnetic fields that stimulate long-term potentiation." *International journal of neuroscience* 79.3-4 (1994): 191-197.

[39] **Squire**, Larry R. "The legacy of patient HM for neuroscience." *Neuron* 61.1 (2009): 6-9.

[40] Image by Paul Doherty, http://www.exo.net/~pauld/ reproduced and modified under the Fair Use Act.

[41] **Bancaud**, Jean, et al. "Anatomical origin of déjà vu and vivid 'memories' in human temporal lobe epilepsy." *Brain* 117.1 (1994): 71-90.

[42] **Kitchener** N. "Alice in Wonderland syndrome". *International Journal of Child Neuropsychiatry.* 2004;1:107–12. 10

[43] **Mehta**, Urvakhsh Meherwan, et al. "Phenomenological and Diagnostic Implications of Paraschemazia: A Case Report." *Turkish journal of psychiatry* 26.2 (2015): 138.

[44] **Touge**, T., et al. "[A case of posterior cerebral artery territory infarction with micropsia as the chief complaint]." *Rinsho shinkeigaku= Clinical neurology*30.8 (1990): 894-897.

[45] **Laudate**, Thomas M., and Aaron P. Nelson.
"Macropsia." *Encyclopedia of Clinical Neuropsychology.* Springer
New York, 2011. 1506-1506.

[46] **JOBST**, BARBARA C., DAVID W. ROBERTS, and PETER D.
WILLIAMSON. "Occipital lobe nonconvulsive status
epilepticus." *Nonconvulsive Status Epilepticus* (2008): 139.

[47] **Doll**, Anselm, et al. "Mindful attention to breath regulates
emotions via increased amygdala–prefrontal cortex
connectivity." *NeuroImage* 134 (2016): 305-313.

[48] **Bódizs**, Róbert, et al. "Human parahippocampal activity: non-REM
and REM elements in wake–sleep transition." *Brain research
bulletin* 65.2 (2005): 169-176.

[49] **De Gennaro**, Luigi, et al. "How we remember the stuff that
dreams are made of: neurobiological approaches to the brain
mechanisms of dream recall."*Behavioural brain research* 226.2
(2012): 592-596.

[50] **Blagrove**, Mark, Perrine Ruby, and Jean-Baptiste Eichenlaub.
"Dreams are made of memories, but maybe not for
memory." *Behavioral and Brain Sciences* 36.06 (2013): 609-610.

[51] **Corsi**-Cabrera, María, et al. "Human amygdala activation during
rapid eye movements of rapid eye movement sleep: an intracranial
study." *Journal of Sleep Research* (2016).

[52] **Yu**, Bin, et al. "Different neural circuitry is involved in physiological
and psychological stress-induced PTSD-like "nightmares" in
rats." *Scientific reports* 5 (2015).

[53] **De Gennaro**, Luigi, et al. "Amygdala and hippocampus volumetry
and diffusivity in relation to dreaming." *Human brain mapping* 32.9
(2011): 1458-1470.

[54] **Spoormaker**, Victor I., Michael Czisch, and Florian Holsboer. "REM
sleep, hippocampus, and memory processing: insights from
functional neuroimaging studies." *Behavioral and Brain
Sciences* 36.06 (2013): 629-630.

[55] **Horowitz**, Mardi J., and John E. Adams. "Hallucinations on brain stimulation: evidence for revision of the Penfield hypothesis." *Origin and mechanisms of hallucinations*. Springer US, 1970. 13-22.

[56] See **Edelman**, Gerald, "The Remembered Present", Basic Books, 1990

[57] **Illman**, Nathan A., et al. "Deja experiences in temporal lobe epilepsy." *Epilepsy research and treatment* 2012 (2012).

[58] **Martin**, Chris B., et al. "Déjà vu in unilateral temporal-lobe epilepsy is associated with selective familiarity impairments on experimental tasks of recognition memory." *Neuropsychologia* 50.13 (2012): 2981-2991.

[59] This concept is inspired by Bancaud's article on the subject. Bancaud, Jean, et al. "Anatomical origin of déjà vu and vivid 'memories' in human temporal lobe epilepsy." *Brain* 117.1 (1994): 71-90.

[60] **Karanian**, Jessica M., and Scott D. Slotnick. "False memory for context activates the parahippocampal cortex." *Cognitive neuroscience* 5.3-4 (2014): 186-192.

[61] **Moulin**, Chris JA. "Disordered recognition memory: recollective confabulation." *Cortex* 49.6 (2013): 1541-1552.

[62] **Irish**, Muireann, et al. "Grey and white matter correlates of recent and remote autobiographical memory retrieval—insights from the dementias." *PloS one* 9.11 (2014): e113081.

[63] **Marchand** WR, "Neural mechanisms of mindfulness and meditation: Evidence from neuroimaging studies." *World Journal of Radiology*. 2014 Jul 28;6(7):471-9.

See also: **Engström**, Maria, et al. "Functional magnetic resonance imaging of hippocampal activation during silent mantra meditation." *The Journal of Alternative and Complementary Medicine* 16.12 (2010): 1253-1258.

[64] **Persinger**, Dr. Michael A., Personal communication.

[65] **Guterstam**, Arvid, et al. "Decoding illusory self-location from activity in the human hippocampus." *Frontiers in human neuroscience* 9 (2015).

[66] **Blanke**, Olaf, et al. "Out-of-body experience and autoscopy of neurological origin." *Brain* 127.2 (2004): 243-258.

[67] **Persinger**, Michael A., et al. "Experimental elicitation of an out of body experience and concomitant cross-hemispheric electroencephalographic coherence." *NeuroQuantology* 8.4 (2010).

[68] **Smith**, Andra M., and Claude Messier. "Voluntary out-of-body experience: an fMRI study." *Frontiers in human neuroscience* 8 (2014).

[69] **Venkatasubramanian**, Ganesan, et al. "Investigating paranormal phenomena: Functional brain imaging of telepathy." *International journal of yoga* 1.2 (2008): 66.

[70] *Dogs That Know When Their Owners Are Coming Home: And Other Unexplained Powers of Animals*, by Rupert Sheldrake, is one of the main work in this area, though it's critics take issue with Sheldrake's methods.   Of course, the phenomenon only has to be demonstrated once to be validated.

[71] **Weldon**, Mary Susan, and Julie L. Jackson-Barrett. "Why do pictures produce priming on the word-fragment completion test? A study of encoding and retrieval factors." *Memory & Cognition* 21.4 (1993): 519-528.

[72] **Peres**, Julio Fernando, et al. "Neuroimaging during trance state: a contribution to the study of dissociation." *PloS one* 7.11 (2012): e49360.   NOTE: This study found a *decrease* in left hippocampal activity, which would allow it's counterpart on the right to add more to the moment. This study used mediums who channeled "automatic writing" from the spirits.

[73] **Bird**, Chris M., et al. "Establishing the boundaries: the hippocampal contribution to imagining scenes." *The Journal of Neuroscience* 30.35 (2010): 11688-11695.

[74] **Villablanca**, Jaime R. "Why do we have a caudate nucleus." *Acta*

neurobiologiae experimentalis 70.1 (2010): 95-105.

[75] **Burgaleta**, Miguel, et al. "Bilingualism at the core of the brain. Structural differences between bilinguals and monolinguals revealed by subcortical shape analysis." *NeuroImage* 125 (2016): 437-445.

[76] **Wittfoth**, Matthias, et al. "On emotional conflict: interference resolution of happy and angry prosody reveals valence-specific effects." *Cerebral Cortex*(2009): bhp106.

[77] **Burgaleta**, Miguel, et al. "Bilingualism at the core of the brain. Structural differences between bilinguals and monolinguals revealed by subcortical shape analysis." *NeuroImage* 125 (2016): 437-445.

[78] **Acevedo**, Bianca P., et al. "Neural correlates of long-term intense romantic love." *Social cognitive and affective neuroscience* (2011): nsq092.

[79] **Noriuchi**, M., and Y. Kikuchi. "[Neural basis of maternal behavior]." *Seishin shinkeigaku zasshi= Psychiatria et neurologia Japonica* 115.6 (2012): 630-634.

[80] **Matsuda**, Yoshi-Taka, et al. "Auditory observation of infant-directed speech by mothers: experience-dependent interaction between language and emotion in the basal ganglia." *Frontiers in human neuroscience* 8 (2014).

[81] **Beauregard**, Mario, et al. "The neural basis of unconditional love." *Psychiatry Research: Neuroimaging* 172.2 (2009): 93-98.

[82] **Kokal**, Idil, et al. "Synchronized drumming enhances activity in the caudate and facilitates prosocial commitment-if the rhythm comes easily." *PLoS One*6.11 (2011): e27272.

[83] Public domain image from Wiki Commons.

[84] **Engström**, Maria, and Birgitta Söderfeldt. "Brain activation during compassion meditation: a case study." *The Journal of Alternative and Complementary Medicine* 16.5 (2010): 597-599.

[85] **Blood**, Anne J., and Robert J. Zatorre. "Intensely pleasurable responses to music correlate with activity in brain regions implicated

in reward and emotion." *Proceedings of the National Academy of Sciences* 98.20 (2001): 11818-11823.

[86] **Grewe**, Oliver, et al. "How Does Music Arouse "Chills"?." *Annals of the New York Academy of Sciences* 1060.1 (2005): 446-449.

[87] **Tarr**, Bronwyn, et al. "Synchrony and exertion during dance independently raise pain threshold and encourage social bonding." *Biology letters* 11.10 (2015): 20150767.

[88] **Lerner**, Yulia, et al. "Eyes wide shut: amygdala mediates eyes-closed effect on emotional experience with music." *PLoS One* 4.7 (2009): e6230.

[89] **Chandrasekhar**, Pammi VS, et al. "Neurobiological regret and rejoice functions for aversive outcomes." *Neuroimage* 39.3 (2008): 1472-1484.

[90] **Rajarethinam**, Rajaprabhakaran, et al. "Hippocampus and amygdala in schizophrenia: assessment of the relationship of neuroanatomy to psychopathology." *Psychiatry Research: Neuroimaging* 108.2 (2001): 79-87.

[91] **Shurkin**, Joel. "News Feature: Animals that self-medicate." *Proceedings of the National Academy of Sciences* 111.49 (2014): 17339-17341.

[92] **Krief**, Sabrina, et al. "[Great apes: who are they? Are they able to self-medicate?]." *Bulletin de l'Academie nationale de medecine* 195.8 (2011): 1927-35.

[93] **Eisenberger**, Naomi I., et al. "In sickness and in health: the co-regulation of inflammation and social behavior." *Neuropsychopharmacology* (2016).

[94] **Koelsch**, Stefan. "Towards a neural basis of music-evoked emotions." *Trends in cognitive sciences* 14.3 (2010): 131-137.

[95] **Venkatasubramanian**, Ganesan, et al. "Investigating paranormal phenomena: Functional brain imaging of telepathy." *International journal of yoga* 1.2 (2008): 66.

[96] **Sumner**, Rachel C., et al. "Hemispheric lateralisation and immune function: A systematic review of human research." *Journal of neuroimmunology* 240 (2011): 1-12.

This reference calls for a little explanation. This study, which compared 11 other studies (a meta-analysis), revealed a relationship between weaker left hemisphere function and poorer immune function, and weaker right hemisphere function and stronger immune functioning. Note carefully that ___weaker___ function in the brain's two hemispheres were correlated with levels of immune system health. When the right side is stronger, immune system function should then, be lowered. When the left side of the brain is stronger, immune function should be expected to have higher levels. Examining compromised functions in the brain is an unusual way of studying the immune system, but perfectly scientific. It's actually an elegant way of laying out the information.

[97] **Hecht**, David. "Depression and the hyperactive right-hemisphere."*Neuroscience research* 68.2 (2010): 77-87.

[98] **Barak**, Yoram. "The immune system and happiness." *Autoimmunity reviews*5.8 (2006): 523-527.

[99] **Koch**, H. J., et al. "Relation between laterality and immune response after acute cerebral schemia." *Neuroimmunomodulation* 13.1 (2006): 8-12. This was based on comparisons of 56 stroke patients.

[100] Dawn **Foster** "Is mindfulness making us ill?" The Guardian, Saturday 23 January 2016 http://www.theguardian.com/lifeandstyle/2016/jan/23/is-mindfulness-making-us-ill

[101] **Pesce**, Mirko, et al. "Positive Correlation Between Serum Interleukin-1β and State Anger in Rugby Athletes." *Aggressive behavior* 39.2 (2013): 141-148.

[102] **Gouin**, Jean-Philippe, et al. "The influence of anger expression on wound healing." *Brain, Behavior, and Immunity* 22.5 (2008): 699-708.

[103] **Weil**, Andrew, "Spontaneous Healing : How to Discover and Embrace Your Body's Natural Ability to Maintain and Heal Itself" Ballantine Books (April 4, 2000)

[104] **Stewart** JL, Levin-Silton R, Sass SM, Heller W, Miller GA. "Anger style, psychopathology, and regional brain activity" *Emotion*. 2008 Oct;8(5):701-13.

[105] **Gidron** Y, Gaygısız E, Lajunen T. "Hostility, driving anger, and dangerous driving: the emerging role of hemispheric preference". *Accident Analysis and Prevention*. 2014 Dec;73:236-41.

[106] **Kawasaki**, Masahiro, et al. "Inter-brain synchronization during coordination of speech rhythm in human-to-human social interaction." *Scientific reports* 3 (2013): 1692.

[107] **Dumas**, Guillaume, et al. "Inter-brain synchronization during social interaction." *PloS one* 5.8 (2010): e12166.

[108] **Dumas**, Guillaume, et al. "Anatomical connectivity influences both intra-and inter-brain synchronizations." *PloS one* 7.5 (2012): e36414.

[109] **Toppi**, J., et al. "Graph theory in brain-to-brain connectivity: A simulation study and an application to an EEG hyperscanning experiment." *2015 37th Annual International Conference of the IEEE Engineering in Medicine and Biology Society (EMBC)*. IEEE, 2015.

[110] **Halasa**, Tariq K., et al. "Human brain-to-brain interface." *World neurosurgery* 84.6 (2015): 1507-1508.

[111] **Rao**, Rajesh PN, et al. "A direct brain-to-brain interface in humans." *PloS one* 9.11 (2014): e111332.

[112] **Grau**, Carles, et al. "Conscious brain-to-brain communication in humans using non-invasive technologies." *PLoS One* 9.8 (2014): e105225.

[113] **Charman**, Robert A. "Placing healers, healees, and healing into a wider research context." *The Journal of Alternative and*

*Complementary Medicine*6.2 (2000): 177-180.

[114] **Persinger**, Michael A., et al. "Correlated cerebral events between physically and sensory isolated pairs of subjects exposed to yoked circumcerebral magnetic fields." *Neuroscience Letters* 486.3 (2010): 231-234.

[115] **Capps**, Lisa L. "Ua neeb khu a Hmong American healing ceremony." *Journal of Holistic Nursing* 29.2 (2011): 98-106.

[116] **Schiff**, Jeannette Wagemakers, and Kerrie Moore. "The impact of the sweat lodge ceremony on dimensions of well-being." *American Indian and Alaska native mental health research (Online)* 13.3 (2006): 48.

[117] **Vinesett**, Ava L., Miurel Price, and Kenneth H. Wilson. "Therapeutic Potential of a Drum and Dance Ceremony Based on the African Ngoma Tradition." *The Journal of Alternative and Complementary Medicine* 21.8 (2015): 460-465.

[118] **Green**, Stuart A. "Surgeons and shamans: the placebo value of ritual."*Clinical orthopaedics and related research* 450 (2006): 249-254.

[119] **Jaremka**, Lisa M., et al. "Loneliness promotes inflammation during acute stress." *Psychological science* 24.7 (2013): 1089-1097.

[120] **Arranz**, L., et al. "[Social isolation during old age worsens cognitive, behavioral and immune impairment]." *Revista espanola de geriatria y gerontologia* 44.3 (2008): 137-142.

[121] **Lissoni**, Paolo, et al. "A spiritual approach in the treatment of cancer: relation between faith score and response to chemotherapy in advanced non-small cell lung cancer patients." *In Vivo* 22.5 (2008): 577-581.

[122] Open-source image by Bob Hall, from Wiki Commons.

[123] **Astin** JA, Stone J, Abrams DI, Moore DH, Couey P, Buscemi R, Targ E. "The efficacy of distant healing for human immunodeficiency virus--results of a randomized trial." *Alternative Therapies in Health*

and Medicine. 2006 Nov-Dec;12(6):36-41

[124] **Aviles** JM, Whelan SE, Hernke DA, Williams BA, Kenny KE, O'Fallon WM, Kopecky SL. "Intercessory prayer and cardiovascular disease progression in a coronary care unit population: a randomized controlled trial." *Mayo Clinic Proceedings.* 2001 Dec;76(12):1192-8.

[125] **Boelens** PA, Reeves RR, Replogle WH, Koenig HG. "A randomized trial of the effect of prayer on depression and anxiety." *International Journal of Psychiatry in Medicine.* 2009;39(4):377-92.

[126] **Leibovici** L. "Effects of remote, retroactive intercessory prayer on outcomes in patients with bloodstream infection: randomised controlled trial." *BMJ (Clincal Research Edition).* 2001 Dec 22-29;323(7327):1450-1.

[127] **Ai** AL, Peterson C, Tice TN, Huang B, Rodgers W, Bolling SF. "The influence of prayer coping on mental health among cardiac surgery patients: the role of optimism and acute distress." *Journal of Health Psychology.* 2007 Jul;12(4):580-96.

[128] **Turner**, D. D. "Just another drug? A philosophical assessment of randomised controlled studies on intercessory prayer." *Journal of medical ethics* 32.8 (2006): 487-490.

[129] **Murphy**, Todd Sacred Pathways; The brain's role in religious and Mystic Experience", Createspace Publishers, 2015.

[130] **Seto**, Akira, et al. "Detection of extraordinary large bio-magnetic field strength from human hand during external Qi emission." *Acupuncture & electro-therapeutics research* 17.2 (1992): 75-94.

[131] **Hisamitsu**, Tadashi, et al. "Emission of extremely strong magnetic fields from the head and whole body during oriental breathing exercises." *Acupuncture & electro-therapeutics research* 21.3-4 (1996): 219-227.

[132] https://karmu.wordpress.com/page/2/ Retrieved 08-16-2016

[133] **Razali**, S. M. "Conversion disorder: a case report of treatment with the Main Puteri, a Malay shamanastic healing ceremony." *European psychiatry* 14.8 (1999): 470-472.

[134] **Eliade**, Mircea "Shamanism: Archaic techniques of ecstasy." *Princeton: Princeton UniversityPress. 1964.*

[135] **Goller**, Aviva I., et al. "Mirror-touch synaesthesia in the phantom limbs of amputees." *Cortex* 49.1 (2013): 243-251.

[136] **Banissy**, Michael J., and Jamie Ward. "Mirror-touch synesthesia is linked with empathy." *Nature neuroscience* 10.7 (2007): 815-816.

[137] **Brogaard**, Berit, Simo Vanni, and Juha Silvanto. "Seeing mathematics: perceptual experience and brain activity in acquired synesthesia." *Neurocase* 19.6 (2013): 566-575.

[138] **Hayasaki**, Erika "The neurologist with mirror-touch synesthesia" http://theweek.com/articles/576530/neurologist-mirrortouch-synesthesia

[139] https://psmag.com/this-doctor-knows-exactly-how-you-feel-f61315e851e7 "...a mirror-touch synesthete from San Francisco, wanted to be a physical therapist. But she couldn't get past the injuries she would have witnessed daily. "The synesthetic pain on a constant basis would have been too much for me to tolerate," she said. So she became a massage therapist instead, and now spends 35 hours a week exposing herself to the pleasurable sensations that clients feel under her hands, which can feel like "waves of warmth" through her own body."

[140] **Goller**, Aviva I., et al. "Mirror-touch synaesthesia in the phantom limbs of amputees." *Cortex* 49.1 (2013): 243-251.

[141] **Carnegie**, Dale "How to win friends and influence people". Multiple Publishers.

[142] **Talmud**, Shabbat 55a, Sanhedrin 64a.

81593948R00117

Made in the USA
Columbia, SC
04 December 2017